GCSE Maths Coursework Companion

CW00421410

Contents

Pearson Education Limited
Edinburgh Gate
Harlow
Essex
CM20 2JE
England

www.longman.co.uk

First published 2003
ISBN 0 582 79599 0

Design by Ken Vail Graphic Design, Cambridge

Printed in the UK by Scotprint, Haddington

The publisher's policy is to use paper manufactured from sustainable forests.

Acknowledgements

The publisher would like to thank Kevin Evans and Paul Metcalf for their advice on the manuscript.

Introduction

The aim of this book is to give you, as a student taking GCSE Maths Coursework, advice on how to get the best possible mark. This is done by giving advice on the two types of coursework that you will be asked to do.

This book covers all exam boards at all tiers of assessment, and will give you:
- general advice about planning and doing your coursework
- a list of the criteria to gain a set number of marks and explanations of those criteria
- a sample task showing you how to get the marks
- a checklist to help you assess if you have done everything you need to.

A good coursework mark can easily make a difference in the final grade that you get for GCSE Maths. So read this book carefully to find out how you can get the best possible mark in your GCSE Maths Coursework.

Good luck!

Keith Gordon, July 2003

What is maths coursework?

Maths coursework is an investigation into a mathematical problem. Coursework allows you to develop your own ideas and take the time to investigate an area of mathematics in more depth than usual. Your account of this investigation is marked and counts towards your final exam grade.

You can do coursework at your own pace, so you can work without the pressure of time that you will have in the written exams. You will normally have about two weeks in the classroom and at home to complete a coursework task.

The most important thing in GCSE Maths coursework is your actual investigation, not just the answer you get at the end. So it is important that you keep a good account of all the decisions you have made, the working you have done, and any results you have collected on the way to your final answer.

The two tasks

You will do two pieces of coursework for GCSE Maths. The first will be a task based on *Using and Applying Mathematics*. The second will be a *Handling Data* task. The two tasks are different in the way they are assessed and in what you are expected to do.

Using and Applying Mathematics (also called Assessment Objective 1 or AO1 by the exam boards) covers the topics of Number; Algebra; and Shape, Space and Measures. **This will be called the AO1 task throughout the book**.

Handling Data (also called Assessment Objective 4 or AO4 by the exam boards) covers the topic of handling data, which is also known as statistics. **This will be called the AO4 task throughout the book**.

How does coursework affect your final mark?

Coursework counts for 20% of your final mark. The other 80% of marks come from written exams.

| Coursework 20% | + | Examination 80% | = | Final total 100% |

Your coursework is marked out of a total of 48 marks. Your mark is then scaled according to the exam board that marks your coursework and the tier you are entered in.

Different specifications

There are three exam boards in England. These are:
- Assessment and Qualifications Alliance (AQA)
- Oxford, Cambridge and RSA Examinations (OCR)
- EDEXCEL (this used to be the London Board).

There are also two other boards:
- CCEA (covers Northern Ireland)
- WJEC (covers Wales).

The criteria for marking your coursework are the same whichever board you take your exam with.

How coursework is marked

Your coursework will be marked in one of two possible ways.

Teacher-marked work

Your maths teachers can decide to mark the coursework themselves. In this case, they will get together to check that they are all marking to the same standards. This is called *internal standardisation*. The board will also ask for a sample of about 20 students' work. The moderator will check that the marks given in the sample are the same that the board would give. Your school's marking is either accepted as accurate or it is adjusted. Your mark could change after this moderation step.

Board-marked work

If the exam board is marking the coursework then it is all sent to the board. The mark that comes back from the board will be the final mark.

Whether your teachers or the board mark your coursework the same lists of criteria are used to assess it.

Criteria

Your work is marked to a set of criteria. These criteria show what you need to do to attain a certain number of marks. The criteria for each task (AO1 and AO4) have three strands. Each strand is marked out of 8. This means your work is marked out of 24 for each task (or out of 48 overall).

The criteria and explanations of the criteria are given later in the book. As you work through the book you will learn more about the criteria. It is essential you understand these if you want to get as high a mark as possible.

How to use this book

Before you start to look at the information for each task you should first find out which tier you are entered for in the exam. There are three tiers for GCSE Maths: *Foundation tier* (covering grades G to D), *Intermediate tier* (covering grades E to B) and *Higher tier* (covering grades C to A*).

For each task at each tier there is:
- advice on planning and carrying out the task
- the criteria for earning marks at that tier
- a sample task that gains full marks at that tier
- suggestions for how the sample task could be improved to get the next level of marks (*Foundation* and *Intermediate tier* only)
- checklists to make sure you have done everything you need to.

For each task at each tier you will see the criteria for earning a set number of marks and a sample task showing how those marks are achieved. In each strand, there is an approximate link between a mark of 3 and grade F; a mark of 5 and grade C; and a mark of 7 and grade A. For each mark in the criteria, which are given by the exam boards, there is an explanation in the shaded box showing what it means. Here is an example.

AO1 1/5

Starting from problems or contexts that have been presented to them, candidates introduce questions of their own, which generate fuller solutions.

- You look not only at the original problem but you change a feature of the problem and investigate that. For example, if the original problem was about squares, you could look at the same problem using rectangles.

AO1 1/5 means that this is the criterion to achieve 5 marks in Strand 1 of the AO1 task.

Throughout the sample tasks there are advice boxes showing two things.
1. Criteria boxes show where in the sample task the marks are gained.
2. Moderator's tips give key advice about carrying out and presenting coursework to make sure you gain all the marks you deserve.

Here is an example.

Square (n)	Number of grains of rice (g)	2^n	Cumulative total grains (t)	$2^n - 1$
1	1	2	1	1
2	2	4	3	3

AO1 1/5

Ben introduces the total number of grains (Cumulative total). This extends a feature of the problem. He also introduces powers. The use of powers has allowed Ben to compare the number of grains on each square and the total number of grains.

Moderator's **TIP**

Explain why you are going to use a table. Usually it is to put your results in a logical form that helps to spot patterns.

At the end of the sections for each task at each tier there is a checklist. This will help you check that the work you have done covers the criteria for that number of marks.

The *Using and Applying Mathematics* task – A01

How the AO1 task is marked

Your work will be marked against criteria (given on pages 7, 11 and 19) in three strands.

Strand one is called *Making and monitoring decisions to solve problems*. This strand is about how you plan your task, how you start it and how you develop it.

Strand two is called *Communicating mathematically*. This strand is about how you explain your task, how you reflect on the results and about the mathematics that you use.

Strand three is called *Developing the skills of mathematical reasoning*. This strand is about how you look for patterns, formulae and solutions to your task, how you check your results and how you alter your approach in light of your results so far.

General advice for approaching the AO1 task

Always make sure that you have a plan for approaching the problem you have been given. It does not matter if you change this plan as you go along, so long as you record how and why you changed it. Your plan can be quite a simple statement of what you intend to do. For example, in the domino problem starting on page 8 you might look at the number of dominoes in 1-spot, 2-spot and 3-spot sets to see if there is a pattern. Later in the task you might change your plan to find a formula for the number of dominoes in an *n*-spot set. You would record the change in your plan and give a reason for it.

Always record all your results. An easy way to do this is to use tables; that way you can record results of different things and compare them. For example, in the domino problem you could record, for each spot number, the total number of dominoes in that set, and the differences between the total numbers of dominoes in each set. By putting the results in a table, any patterns become easier to see.

Keep your work concise. This means that it is not necessary to do pages and pages of calculations or write large amounts to get good marks. A good approach is to do enough calculations or examples to see if you can find a pattern. Once you have spotted a pattern, make a prediction about an example where you have not already calculated the result using the pattern you have found. Then test this prediction. It is a good idea to do more than one test of the pattern or formula you think you have found.

Use ICT to help you. If you have to do a lot of repeated calculations to find a pattern you could speed this up by using a spreadsheet to help you.

Remember to check all your work. Recurring mistakes can prevent you from gaining the marks you deserve.

Foundation tier

Advice for Foundation tier

- Before you start, think about a plan that allows you to solve the problem.
- Break the problem down into smaller tasks that make solving it easier.
- Make sure the maths you do is appropriate to this tier.

A01 Criteria for marks of 3 and 4   **What this means**

A01 1/3

In order to carry through tasks and solve mathematical problems, candidates identify and obtain necessary information; they check their results, considering whether these are sensible.

- The work you do is relevant to the problem, e.g. if the problem is about area you don't start by looking at volume.
- Looking at the problem you decide what is needed to solve it. For example, if the problem is about area you realise that you will need some measurements of area.
- When checking your results you realise if you have a result that seems wrong, e.g. $20 \times 30 = 60$ (it should say $= 600$).

A01 2/3

Candidates show understanding of situations by describing them mathematically using symbols, words and diagrams.

- You show your results in a table (with headings), a list of numbers or a clearly labelled diagram.
- You try to explain your results.

A01 3/3

Candidates make general statements of their own, based on evidence they have produced, and give an explanation of their reasoning.

- You spot a pattern or make a mathematical statement about your results. For example, you might say 'as the number of spots is increased by 1 the difference in the total number of possible dominoes goes up by 1 more each time'.
- You link your statement or pattern to your results.

A01 1/4

Candidates carry through substantial tasks and solve quite complex problems by breaking them down into smaller, more manageable tasks.

- When you look at a problem you break it down into smaller steps in order to solve it. For example, you might get some results, put them in a table, and then look for a pattern.
- The way you break the problem down makes it easier for you to solve it.

A01 2/4

Candidates interpret, discuss and synthesise information presented in a variety of mathematical forms. Their writing explains and informs their use of diagrams.

- You show your results in at least two different ways, e.g. a table and a diagram.
- You link the two sets of results explaining the connections.

A01 3/4

Candidates are beginning to give a mathematical justification for their generalisations; they test them by checking particular cases.

- When you have spotted a pattern, or made a mathematical statement, you then go on to test the pattern using an example you don't already know the result for.

Domino boxes

The following task gets a mark of 4 in each strand.

A 1-spot domino set has 3 dominoes in it.

A 2-spot domino set has 6 dominoes in it.

How many dominoes are there in a regular 6-spot set?
Investigate further.

Davina's answer

First of all I will look at a 3-spot set.

A 3-spot set is a set of dominoes with 3 as the biggest number on either half of a domino. This means that it starts with double blank and ends with a double 3.

I will draw all the dominoes in a 3-spot set.

This gives a total of 10 dominoes.

I also figured out that if you have a 0-spot set there is only 1 domino, which is double blank.

Now I think I can see a pattern and I am going to put my results in a table.

Maximum number of spots on either half of a domino in the set	Total number of dominoes in the set
0	1
1	3
2	6
3	10

+2
+3
+4

> The difference in total numbers increases by 1 every time.

Moderator's TIP

By making this statement Davina shows she understands the problem. You should always explain the problem in your own words to show that you understand it.

A01 1/3

Davina has made some progress on the task. It is clear from her writing that she has a plan to follow and that she understands the problem.

Moderator's TIP

Always write everything down. Even though it is obvious that there are 10 dominoes and the results are going into a table, say so anyway.

A01 2/3

Get results into a table as soon as possible. It shows your results clearly and it is easier to spot patterns.

Moderator's TIP

If you spot a rule, write it down and highlight it in some way, e.g. put a box around it or use a highlighter pen, but don't forget to explain it.

I have noticed that the difference between the total number of dominoes goes up by 1 every time the maximum number of spots goes up by 1.

From 0 to 1 the difference is 2.

From 1 to 2 the difference is 3.

From 2 to 3 the difference is 4.

If my idea is true I predict there should be a difference of 5 between the total number of dominoes in a 3-spot set and a 4-spot set. This will give a total of 10 + 5 = 15 dominoes in a 4-spot set.

I will test this to see if it is true.

This is a 4-spot set.

I was right, there are 15 dominoes in a 4-spot set.

I think I can see why it goes up 1 more each time.

Every time you increase the set number by one more spot there will be a new blank-spot, one-spot, two-spot and so on up to double-spot extra dominoes.

So for 5 spots there will be these extra dominoes.

This gives 6 more dominoes.

I can now work out how many dominoes there will be in a normal 6-spot set.

For a 5 spot set there are 15 + 6 = 21 dominoes.

For a 6-spot set there will be 21 + 7 = 28 dominoes.

So, there are 28 dominoes in a 6-spot set.

A01 3/3

Davina states a rule that is correct for her results. This is a generalisation

A01 1/4

By looking at how the number of dominoes increases for a 1-spot, 2-spot, 3-spot set, etc. Davina is breaking down the task so that she can spot a pattern.

Moderator's **TIP**

When you spot a rule use it to make a prediction and test your prediction straight away.

Moderator's **TIP**

Don't forget to write down that you are going to test it.

A01 3/4

Davina tests her rule and explains why the difference in the number of dominoes increases by one each time a new set is considered.

Moderator's **TIP**

Davina's explanation is a bit vague, so she has used an example with 5-spot dominoes. Always back up explanations with an example if you can.

A01 2/4

Davina links together all her results and solves the original problem. Throughout the work her table and diagrams have been linked.

<u>Conclusion</u>

I have now found the patterns for how many dominoes there are in a 6-spot set.

The difference increases by 1 every time.

1, 3, 6, 10, 15, 21, 28, ...

I can use the patterns to find the number of dominoes on any set of dominoes.

> **Moderator's TIP**
>
> It is always worth doing a conclusion to bring all your work together.

How to get the next mark up

Davina's task gets a mark of 4 in all three strands. If she wanted to try to get a mark of 5 in all three strands Davina needs to extend the problem. She could try to find some formulae using algebra. She could use the results and patterns of numbers to try and find formulae for the number of dominoes and the number of spots in any set of dominoes.

Checklist for the AO1 task

Foundation tier

☐ Have you stated the aim of your task at the beginning?

☐ Have you explained what you are doing at every stage?

☐ Have you broken the task down into simpler tasks?

☐ Have you put your results in a table?

☐ Have you written down all the ideas that you have had?

☐ Have you explained the connection between your tables, graphs and diagrams?

☐ Have you tested any rules that you have come up with?

☐ Have you used at least two different ways (tables, graphs, diagrams) to back up your results and ideas?

☐ Have you written a sensible conclusion?

Intermediate tier
Advice for Intermediate tier

- Make a plan for investigating the problem. Remember, you can modify your plan as you go along.
- Aim to extend your investigation beyond solving the original problem.
- Make sure the maths you do is appropriate to this tier.

AO1 Criteria for marks of 5 and 6   What this means

AO1 1/5

Starting from problems or contexts that have been presented to them, candidates introduce questions of their own, which generate fuller solutions.

- You look not only at the original problem but you change a feature of the problem and investigate that. For example, if the original problem was about squares, you could look at the same problem using rectangles.

AO1 2/5

Candidates examine critically and justify their choice of mathematical presentation, considering alternative approaches and explaining improvements they have made.

- You should show your results in more than one way. For example, you might put your results in a table and use this to find an algebraic formula. Alternatively, a graph can show a result from a different approach.
- You should always explain why you have tried a different approach.

AO1 3/5

Candidates justify their generalisations or solutions, showing some insight into the mathematical structure of the situation being investigated. They appreciate the difference between mathematical explanation and experimental evidence.

- You explain where a formula comes from by relating it to the original problem.
- You test your formula or rule.
- If you have used a graph you explain why the graph backs up your other work.

AO1 1/6

Candidates develop and follow alternative approaches. They reflect on their own lines of enquiry when exploring mathematical tasks; in doing so they introduce and use a range of mathematical techniques.

- You extend the task by using a different approach. For example, if the problem used Pythagoras' Theorem you might look at a similar problem by using trigonometry.
- You use a range of algebraic techniques.

AO1 2/6

Candidates convey mathematical meaning through consistent use of symbols.

- The new mathematics you introduce must be done correctly and you need to be consistent.
- Make sure that you use = signs correctly, i.e. the expressions on either side of the = sign must be *equal*. It is incorrect to write $4a + 2a = 6a \div 2a = 3$ because $4a + 2a \neq 3$.

AO1 3/6

Candidates examine generalisations or solutions reached in an activity, commenting constructively on the reasoning and logic employed, and make further progress in the activity as a result.

- You explain clearly why you have extended the task.
- Your explanation must be logical and relevant to the original task.

The price is rice

The following task gets a mark of 6 in each strand.

Mustafa Fagg, the Sultan of Nicotina, decided to reward the wise man that invented the game of chess.

The wise man was told that he could have his weight in gold or anything else that the Sultan could give him.

The wise man said that he would be happy to have enough food to last him till the end of his days.

'I will have 1 grain of rice on the first square of the chessboard, 2 grains on the second square, 4 grains on the third square, 8 on the fourth square and so on until the 64th square is filled', he said.

'What a fool', thought the Sultan and agreed immediately.

Investigate.

You will need to know that:

The wise man weighs 82 kg

1 lb = 16 oz

1 kg = 2.2 lbs

1 ounce of gold is worth \$346.25

£1 sterling = \$1.71

1 kg rice contains about 1800 grains

1 kg rice is worth £1.20

Ben's answer

Plan

First of all I will work out how much the wise man is worth in gold. Then I will try to work out how much rice the wise man would get from the chessboard.

If this is worth more than his weight in gold then he has made the better choice.

The wise man's worth in gold

I'm trying to work out how much 1 ounce of gold is worth in pounds sterling.

$$346.25 \div 1.71 = £202.4853801 \text{ per oz}$$

Price of one ounce   Exchange rate   Price of one ounce
of gold in dollars   of gold in pounds

I'm now going to work out how much the man is worth in gold.

I know that 1 lb = 16 oz and 2.2 lb = 1 kg.

The man weighs 82 kg, so he weighs 82 kg × 2.2 = 180.4 lb.

This is 180.4 × 16 = 2886.4 oz.

So the man weighs 2886.4 oz.

Moderator's **TIP**

It is always worth writing out a plan so that both you and the person marking your work can see how you intend to go about solving the problem. You can change your plan later as the task develops.

Moderator's **TIP**

Sub headings are useful to show how you are breaking the task up. Make sure you explain what you are doing at each stage.

A01 1/4

This is called a substantial task which means it has to be broken down into different parts to solve it. By working out the value of the man in gold Ben gets a mark of 4 in *Strand one*.

Moderator's **TIP**

Even though the factual information is given in the task statement it is worth repeating to make your work easier to read.

I know that gold is worth £202.453801 per ounce ($346.25 divided by 1.71).

The value of the wise man's weight in gold is:
2886.4 × £202.453801 = £584 362.65

The rice has to be worth more than this, or the man is a fool.

The number of grains of rice on the board

I will now work out how many grains of rice the man has.

On the first square there will be 1 grain of rice. Total = 1.
On the second square there will be 2 grains of rice. Total = 3.
On the third square there will be 4 grains of rice. Total = 7.
On the fourth square there will be 8 grains of rice. Total = 15.

I have noticed that the number of grains of rice on each square goes up: 1, 2, 4, 8, ….
And the total number of grains of rice goes up: 1, 3, 7, 15, ….

I think that I can see a pattern, which has to do with powers of 2. To help me see the pattern I will put my results in a table. If I can spot a pattern then I will be able to work out how many grains of rice the wise man will have by the time the whole chessboard is filled.

I will call the number of the square n.
I will call the number of grains on each square g.
I will call the total number of grains t.

Square (n)	Number of grains of rice (g)	2^n	Cumulative total grains (t)	$2^n - 1$
1	1	2	1	1
2	2	4	3	3
3	4	8	7	7
4	8	16	15	15
5	16	32	31	31
6	32	64	63	63

I can see from the table that the number of grains of rice on square n is: $g = 2^{n-1}$

From the table I can see that the cumulative total is the same as the number of grains of rice on the next square, but one less: $t = 2^n - 1$

I now know the rule for how many grains of rice there are on the nth square.

> Number of grains of rice on a square $g = 2^{n-1}$

> Total number of grains up to that square $t = 2^n - 1$

Moderator's _TIP_
If you come up with an important rule or formula, it is worth highlighting it.

Testing my rule

Moderator's _TIP_
Always test a rule immediately after stating it.

If my rules are true then the number of grains on the seventh square should be 64 and the total number of grains up to the seventh square will be 127.

I will continue the table above to see if this is true.

Square (n)	Number of grains of rice (g)	2^n	Cumulative total grains (t)	$2^n - 1$
6	32	64	63	63
7	64	128	127	127
8	128	256	255	255

A01 3/5
Testing the formula by extending the table above is always worth 3/5 providing the formula is correct and comes from some sensible work. Ben also justifies his formula by using differencing.

I can also show this is true by using differencing.

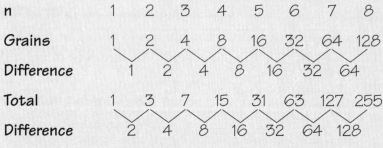

n	1	2	3	4	5	6	7	8
Grains	1	2	4	8	16	32	64	128
Difference		1	2	4	8	16	32	64
Total	1	3	7	15	31	63	127	255
Difference		2	4	8	16	32	64	128

This shows my rule is correct.

Moderator's _TIP_
Always make a comment after testing a rule, even if it is obvious.

Extending the problem

I think the 2 in the formula is because the number of grains of rice on each square doubles each time.

If I make the number of grains triple on each square then the formulae should involve 3 to the power n.

The number of grains on each square: $g = 3^{n-1}$

The total number of grains: $t = 3^n - 1$

A01 1/6
By investigating what happens when the number of grains triples Ben has introduced a mathematical extension to the problem.

I will calculate the number of grains of rice on each square and the total number of grains of rice for the first five squares.

Square (n)	Number of grains of rice on each square (g)	Total number of grains of rice (t)
1	1	1
2	3	4
3	9	13
4	27	40
5	81	121

> **Moderator's TIP**
> Put results in tables. It makes them easier to read. Remember to explain what you are doing.

Testing my formula

If my formula is right then on the fifth square there should be 81 grains of rice and 242 total grains of rice, because:

$$3^{5-1} = 3^4$$
$$= 81$$
$$3^5 - 1 = 242$$

This is not the same as the results in my table.

> **Moderator's TIP**
> Always test any formula you come up with. It doesn't matter if it doesn't work. You can use this to look for a rule that does work.

The rule works for the number of grains but it doesn't work for the total number of grains. My formula gives twice the actual answer.

I will now see what happens when the number of grains on each square is multiplied by four.

Square (n)	Number of grains of rice on each square (g)	Total number of grains of rice (t)
1	1	1
2	4	5
3	16	21
4	64	85
5	256	341

> **Moderator's TIP**
> If a rule doesn't work, don't discard it. You can use a wrong rule to help you with the correct answer.

If my rules are right then there should be 64 grains of rice on the fourth square and 255 grains of rice in total by the fourth square, because:

$$4^{4-1} = 4^3$$
$$= 64$$
$$4^4 - 1 = 255$$

The rule works for the number of grains but doesn't work for the total number of grains. When we multiply the number of grains by 4 on each new square the formula for t gives a value that is **three** times the actual answer: $3 \times 85 = 255$.

When the number of grains was tripled on each new square my formula for t was **twice** the actual answer.

This has given me an idea. ←

Moderator's **TIP**

If you have an idea, write it down straight away and explain it.

The number of grains of rice on the nth square is: $g = m^{n-1}$

The total number of grains up to the nth square is: $t = \dfrac{m^{n-1}}{m-1}$

Where:

n = the square

m = the number that the grains of rice are multiplied by per square in this pattern

g = grains of rice on the square

t = total number of grains up to the square.

Moderator's **TIP**

Always define new variables and repeat definitions of previous ones.

I know the g formula is correct but I am going to test the t formula for multiplying the number of grains by 5.

Therefore $\times 5$ will be: $\quad t = \dfrac{m^{n-1}}{m-1} = \dfrac{5^{n-1}}{4}$

If this is right, the total for 5 squares should be:

$$\frac{5^5 - 1}{4} = \frac{3125 - 1}{4} = \frac{3124}{4} = 781$$

Square (n)	Number of grains of rice on each square (g)	Total number of grains of rice (t)
1	1	1
2	5	6
3	25	31
4	125	156
5	625	781

The rule works. ←

A01 3/6

Ben has recognised the pattern and defined it in symbols and then tested it. So he has used reasoning to make further progress.

So now I know both rules whatever the circumstances are:

n = the square
g = grains of rice on the square
m = the number the grains of rice are multiplied by
t = the total grains of rice on the board.

On the nth
square
$g = m^{n-1}$

Total on board up
to nth square
$$t = \frac{m^{n-1}}{m-1}$$

Finally, I will now return to the original problem and solve it using my rules.

We need to know the total number of grains on the 64 squares of the chessboard when the number of grains is doubled each time. This means I need to use the t formula with $n = 64$ and $m = 2$.

This gives the total number of grains as:

$$t = \frac{m^{64-1}}{m-1} = \frac{2^{64-1}}{2-1} = \frac{2^{64-1}}{1} = 2^{64-1} = 9.223372037 \times 10^{18} \text{ grains}$$

<u>The value of the rice</u>

1 kg rice is worth £1.20.
1800 grains = 1 kg

First I will convert the number of grains into the weight in kg:
$9.223372037 \times 10^{18} \div 1800 = 5.124095576 \times 10^{15}$ kg

Now I will work out the value of this weight of rice:
$5.124095576 \times 10^{15}$ kg $\times 1.20 = £6.148914691 \times 10^{15}$

<u>Conclusion</u>

The rice is worth £6.148914691 × 10^{15}
($\approx$ £6000000000000000)
whereas the man's weight in gold is only worth £584 363
($\approx$ £600000).

The rice is worth about ten thousand million times more than the gold.

The Sultan thought the wise man was foolish but, because the rice was worth so much more, it turned out the Sultan was actually the fool!

A01 2/6

Throughout the project Ben has been consistent with algebra, which is correct. All of his calculations are correct also.

Moderator's **TIP**

Don't forget to write a conclusion and solve the original problem.

How to get the next mark up

To be able to get the next mark up Ben would have to look at an additional variable. For example, he might consider boards that don't start with 1 grain of rice on the first square. He should use algebra to come up with a rule that covers all possible variations: start number, a, and the number of times the grains increase each time, m. He would have to justify this formula using two different methods. The beginning of this is as follows.

I will now use algebra to work out how many grains of rice there would be on the board if there were a on the first square and on the next square this number is multiplied by m.

Square (n)	Number of grains of rice on each square (g)	Total number of grains of rice (t)
1	a	a
2	am	$a + am$
3	am^2	$a + am + am^2$
4	am^3	$a + am + am^2 + am^3$
5	am^4	$a + am + am^2 + am^3 + am^4$

Checklist for the A01 task

Intermediate tier

☐ Have you changed a feature of the task, and explained why you have done so?

☐ Have you used algebra to look for patterns or to justify your numerical results?

☐ Have you changed a mathematical feature of the task?

☐ Have you linked the different ways of showing your results?

☐ Is the mathematics you have used of sufficient standard and are your calculations mostly accurate?

☐ If you have used a spreadsheet have you shown the formulae you have used?

☐ Have you tested each formula you have come up with?

☐ Have you written a sensible conclusion?

Higher tier
Advice for Higher tier

- Start by making a plan that will involve using some higher (grade A) algebra or trigonometry.
- Look for patterns in your results, and make and test hypotheses. Try to form algebraic expressions of the patterns. Justify any formulae you derive.
- Extend the task into a related and more complex one.
- Finally, check for errors (they may prevent you from getting the highest marks).

AO1 Criteria for marks of 7 and 8   What this means

A01 1/7

Candidates analyse alternative approaches to problems involving a number of features or variables. They give detailed reasons for following or rejecting particular lines of enquiry.

- You work on a complex task involving at least three features or variables. For example, you might investigate the quadratic equation $ax^2 + bx + c = 0$, and the effect of a, b and c on the graph $y = ax^2 + bx + c$.
- The work must be relevant to the original problem.

A01 2/7

Candidates use mathematical language and symbols accurately in presenting a convincing reasoned argument.

- You must use algebra or trigonometry and it has to be used correctly.
- You should also explain what you are doing clearly and concisely, and relate your ideas to the algebra using graphs or spreadsheets.

A01 3/7

Candidates' reports include mathematical justifications explaining their solutions to problems involving a number of features or variables.

- You justify your formulae and use of algebra (not just to see if it works with one particular set of numbers).
- You need to show why your formula works by two or more different means. For example, this could be numerical, algebraic, spatial or graphical.

A01 1/8

Candidates consider and evaluate a number of approaches to a substantial task. They explore extensively a context or area of mathematics with which they are unfamiliar. They apply independently a range of appropriate mathematical techniques.

- You may need to use more than one mathematical method to solve the problem.
- You have to take the task beyond the original problem to a level that needs complex mathematics to solve it.

A01 2/8

Candidates use mathematical language and symbols efficiently in presenting a concise reasoned argument.

- The new mathematics you introduce must be done correctly and you need to be consistent.
- The mathematics you do must be concise.

A01 3/8

Candidates provide a mathematically rigorous justification or proof of their solution to a complex problem, considering the conditions under which it remains valid.

- Your explanation must be logical and relevant to the original task and must solve the problem completely.
- You must use algebra to solve the problem.

Dipsticks

The following task gets a mark of 8 in each strand.

Here are three underground storage tanks.

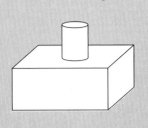 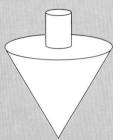 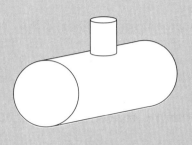

The cylinders on top are the pipes through which the containers are filled and do not need to be considered.

To measure the amount in them a dipstick is used.

Investigate dipsticks to measure the amount in each tank.

Anna's answer

To make the work easier I am going to give all the containers some measurements.

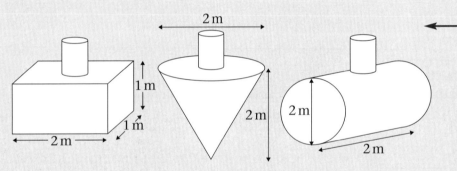

A01 3/5

By assigning numbers Anna breaks down a complicated task into one that is more manageable.

I will start with the cuboid container, as that is the easiest.

The total volume is 2 m³ or 2 000 000 cm³. If the liquid is *d* cm deep then the volume of liquid is:

$$(d \div 100) \times 2 \times 1 = \frac{2d}{100} \text{ m}^3$$

Moderator's **TIP**

If you have a complex problem, you can try it using numbers to give you some ideas about what is happening.

I will put this in a table.

I have just realised that a cubic metre is not a measure of capacity so I will convert to litres.

$$1 \text{ litre} = 1000 \text{ cm}^3$$
$$1 \text{ m}^3 = 1\,000\,000 \text{ cm}^3$$
$$\text{So } 1 \text{ m}^3 = 1000 \text{ litres}$$

Moderator's **TIP**

Always define the units and conversions between units that you use.

When the tank is filled to a depth of d cm, the volume of the liquid is:

$$= \frac{2d}{100} \ m^3$$

$$= \frac{2d \times 1000}{100} \ litres$$

$$= 20 \times d \ litres$$

d (cm)	v (l)
10	200
20	400
30	600
40	800
50	1000
60	1200
70	1400
80	1600
90	1800
100	2000

Using the table I have drawn dipstick 1 on page 27.

This is only good for the $1 \times 1 \times 2$ box.

What about any size of cuboid container?

Total volume of cuboid = $wlh \times 1000$ litres

Volume of liquid = $wld \times 1000$ litres

All lengths will be in metres.

$$So \ \frac{volume \ of \ liquid}{total \ volume} = \frac{wld \times 1000}{wlh \times 1000} = \frac{d}{h}$$

This means the dipstick can be marked off as fractions of the total volume, V.

$$Volume \ of \ liquid = \frac{d \times total \ volume}{h}$$

This is dipstick 2 on page 27.

This has given me an idea about the cone!

A01 2/4

The work so far has been well explained, with a linking table and the calculations leading to the dipstick for a cuboidal tank. The calculations, table and dipstick are different forms of mathematical presentation at this level.

A01 1/5

The change from number to algebra is a change of feature but not enough of a change to be a new area of mathematics.

A01 2/5

Anna has decided to look at algebra and come up with a general rule.

A01 3/5

Anna has related the original problem with numbers to a general case for any volume.

Instead of looking at numbers, I will try to do it with letters.

The volume of the cone is $\frac{1}{3}\pi r^2 h$.

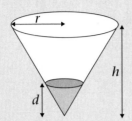

> **A01 1/6**
>
> Anna has reflected on what she has done so far and decided to look at the general case (i.e. use algebra for the other containers). This is a new area of maths.

I don't know the radius but I can use similar triangles to find it.

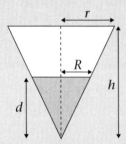

$$\frac{r}{h} = \frac{R}{d}$$

$$\text{so} \quad R = \frac{rd}{h}$$

> **A01 2/6**
>
> Anna has defined the variables (in the diagram) and has used mathematics (similar triangles) at an appropriate level. The algebra has been manipulated correctly.

So volume of liquid $= \frac{1}{3}\pi\left(\frac{rd}{h}\right)^2 d$

$$= \frac{\frac{1}{3}\pi r^2 d^3}{h^2}$$

So $\dfrac{\text{volume of liquid}}{\text{total volume}} = \dfrac{\pi r^2 d^3}{3h^2} \div \dfrac{\pi r^2 h}{3} = \dfrac{d^3}{h^3}$

Therefore, volume of liquid $= \dfrac{d^3 \times \text{total volume}}{h^3}$

$\dfrac{\text{total volume}}{h^3}$ is a constant value so the volume of the liquid is proportional to d^3.

> **A01 3/6**
>
> Davina has made progress on the task and used mathematical reasoning to do this.

This is dipstick 3 on page 27.

Now I can check it with some numbers. This spreadsheet shows the results for the cone I started with (radius = 1 m and height = 2 m).

Depth (m)	Volume of liquid (m³)	Depth cubed (m³)	Volume of liquid/ total volume
0.2	0.002094395	0.008	0.001
0.4	0.016755161	0.064	0.008
0.6	0.056548668	0.216	0.027
0.8	0.134041287	0.512	0.064
1.0	0.261799388	1.0	0.125
1.2	0.452389342	1.728	0.216
1.4	0.71837752	2.744	0.343
1.6	1.072330292	4.096	0.512
1.8	1.52681403	5.832	0.729
2.0	2.094395102	8.0	1.0

The first column is the depth (d), marked off in tenths of the total depth (0.2 m).

The second column is $\frac{1}{3}\pi R^2 d$.

The formula I used was: =(1/3)*PI( )*0.5*0.5*A2^3

> **A01 2/6**
>
> If you are working with spreadsheets you should always show the formula you are using. There is no point just typing in numbers. You must use formulae. If you use a spreadsheet this is another feature and providing it has some relevance will get you at least a 2/6.

The A2 refers to the first column, the depth, and the first row, 0.2. The formula for the depth of 0.4 has A3 instead, the formula for a depth of 0.6 has A4, etc.

which comes from replacing the radius R in $\frac{1}{3}\pi R^2 d$ with $\frac{rd}{h}$ which comes from the similar triangles above.

If $r = 1$ and $h = 2$ this gives $R^2 = \frac{1}{2} \times \frac{1}{2} \times d^2$.

The third column is d^3. The formula is just: $= A2^3$

The fourth column is volume of liquid ÷ total volume.

> **A01 1/7**
>
> The use of algebra, a spreadsheet and linking commentary, all of which are relevant to the problem gets 1/7 as the task is sufficiently complex and three features have been used (volume, radius and depth).

The formula used was: = B2/((1/3)*PI( )*1*1*2)

The fourth column confirms that the divisions marked on my dipstick are correct, i.e. for a depth of $\frac{1}{10}$ of the total depth there is a volume of 0.001 of the total volume, V. This confirms that the volume is proportional to d^3.

This confirms that my rule for dipstick 3 is correct.

> **A01 3/7**
>
> Anna justifies her result by using the spreadsheet, so she brings together algebra, spreadsheets and a numerical justification.

Now I am going to look at the cylinder which is definitely the hardest as the volume doesn't increase linearly.

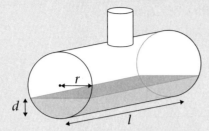

This is the formula:

Volume of prism = cross-sectional area × length

Now I need to work out the cross-sectional area of the liquid.

This is the shaded shape below. θ is the half angle at the centre.

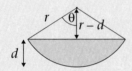 $\cos \theta = \dfrac{r-d}{r}$

> **Moderator's TIP**
> You should always define variables when using algebra or trigonometry and put these onto a diagram if necessary.

Area of sector = $\dfrac{2\theta \times \pi \times r^2}{360}$

Area of triangle = $\frac{1}{2}$ base × height = $r\sin\theta \times (r - d)$

Area of segment = $\dfrac{\theta \times \pi r^2}{180} - r\sin\theta(r - d)$

Volume = $\left[\dfrac{\theta \times \pi r^2}{180} - r\sin\theta(r - d)\right] \times l$

Total volume of cylinder = $\pi r^2 l$

So $\dfrac{\text{volume of liquid}}{\text{total volume}} = \left[\dfrac{\theta \times \pi r^2}{180} - r\sin\theta(r - d)\right] \times l \div (\pi r^2 \times l)$

$= \dfrac{\theta \times \pi r^2}{180 \times \pi r^2} - \dfrac{r^2 \sin\theta}{\pi r^2} + \dfrac{rd\sin\theta}{\pi r^2}$

$= \dfrac{\theta}{180} - \dfrac{\sin\theta}{\pi} + \dfrac{d\sin\theta}{\pi r}$ [1]

> **Moderator's TIP**
> Label equations so you can refer to them later.

This formula is too complicated to find a simple answer to, so I will go back to numbers. I can use the formula to check.

> **A01 2/7**
> The algebra is correct and the formula arrived at is correct. The fact that it is too complicated to work with doesn't stop Anna scoring 2/7.

I am now going to check my formula. To do this I can compare the value of volume of the liquid ÷ the total volume when I use my formula to calculate it and when I find it by other methods.

I can use a spreadsheet to calculate the volume of the liquid ÷ total volume using my formula at set depths.

I will test three different cylinders all of length of 2 m, with radii 1 m, 2 m, and 3 m. For each cylinder I will test when the cylinders are half full, as I know the depth will be the same as the radius and that theta is 90°.

This is the spreadsheet I used to calculate the values. Since Excel works in radians, I had to convert the angle to radians and also reconsider the first part of the formula as if it the angle was in radians,

i.e. $\dfrac{\theta}{180}$ became $\dfrac{\theta}{\pi}$.

	A	B	C	D	E
1	Radius (m) [and depth]	Length (m)	Theta (°)	Theta (radians)	Total volume (m^3)
2	1	2	90	=RADIANS(C2)	=A2^2*B2*PI()
3	2	2	90	=RADIANS(C3)	=A3^2*B3*PI()
4	3	2	90	=RADIANS(C4)	=A4^2*B4*PI()

	F	G
1	Vol. of liq./total vol. [Not using formula]	Vol. of liq./total vol. [Using my formula]
2	=(E2/2)/E2	=(D2/PI())-(SIN(D2)/(PI()))+(A2*SIN(D2)/(A2*PI()))
3	=(E3/2)/E3	=(D3/PI())-(SIN(D3)/(PI()))+(A3*SIN(D3)/(A3*PI()))
4	=(E4/2)/E4	=(D4/PI())-(SIN(D4)/(PI()))+(A4*SIN(D4)/(A4*PI()))

Below are the calculated values. The sixth and seventh columns have the same values. This shows that my formula is correct.

Radius (m) [and depth]	Length (m)	Theta (°)	Theta (radians)	Total volume (m^3)	Vol. of liq./total vol. [Not using formula]	Vol. of liq./total vol. [Using my formula]
1	2	90	1.57079633	6.28318531	0.5	0.5
2	2	90	1.57079633	25.1327412	0.5	0.5
3	2	90	1.57079633	56.5486678	0.5	0.5

In the formulae for volume and θ I had to get help from my teacher because the computer works in radians but my formulae are in degrees.

$360° = 2 × π$ radians, so to convert from degrees to radians you divide by 360 and multiply by $2π$ and vice versa for radians to degrees. I have multiplied by 180 and divided by $π$ as this is the same thing. From this table I can work out the dipstick for the cylinder.

This is dipstick 4 on page 27.

This is the graph of volume against depth.

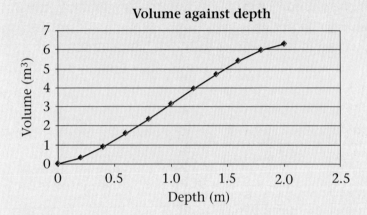

Volume against depth

I have now drawn four dipsticks but looking at them I can see that they are not very practical as they are marked off in uneven decimal intervals.

I thought about this and realised that if I reverse the data and plot the depth against the volume then I get the graph below.

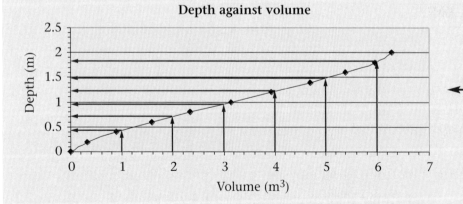

Depth against volume

Drawing lines from the volume on the horizontal axis, up to the plotted line and across to the depth on the vertical axis shows the volume at regular intervals for the different depths.

Moderator's TIP

You are allowed to get help if there is something that you cannot understand. Radians is an A-level topic! Make sure you give a brief description of how it works. You need to show that you have some understanding of the idea.

A01 1/8

The algebra on the previous pages and the use of spreadsheets is of a sufficiently high level to be worth a mark of 8 in *Strand one*. It is relevant to the problem and is used to solve the problem.

A01 2/8

If 1/8 has been awarded and the work is well explained without any unnecessary mathematics then, providing it is all accurate and the algebra is correct, you should also get 2/8.

A01 3/8

This diagram shows a consideration of the practical problems of using a dipstick. All the mathematics on the cylinder is accurate. The correct answer has been achieved using mathematics at a high level; at least three different features – volume, radius and depth – have been investigated using algebra, spreadsheet, graphs; and the practical problems have been coordinated.

The lines I have drawn show the depth for volumes of 1, 2, 3, 4, 5 and 6 m³.

This is dipstick 5 below.

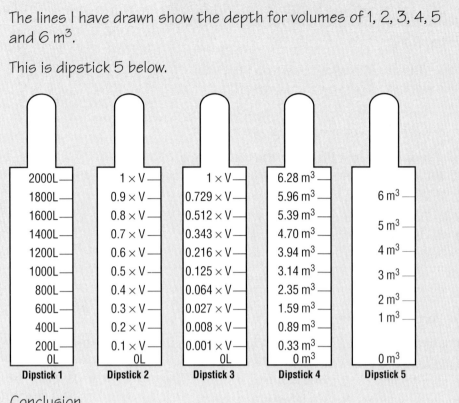

Dipstick 1	Dipstick 2	Dipstick 3	Dipstick 4	Dipstick 5
2000L	$1 \times V$	$1 \times V$	$6.28 \, m^3$	
1800L	$0.9 \times V$	$0.729 \times V$	$5.96 \, m^3$	$6 \, m^3$
1600L	$0.8 \times V$	$0.512 \times V$	$5.39 \, m^3$	$5 \, m^3$
1400L	$0.7 \times V$	$0.343 \times V$	$4.70 \, m^3$	
1200L	$0.6 \times V$	$0.216 \times V$	$3.94 \, m^3$	$4 \, m^3$
1000L	$0.5 \times V$	$0.125 \times V$	$3.14 \, m^3$	$3 \, m^3$
800L	$0.4 \times V$	$0.064 \times V$	$2.35 \, m^3$	$2 \, m^3$
600L	$0.3 \times V$	$0.027 \times V$	$1.59 \, m^3$	$1 \, m^3$
400L	$0.2 \times V$	$0.008 \times V$	$0.89 \, m^3$	
200L	$0.1 \times V$	$0.001 \times V$	$0.33 \, m^3$	
0L	0L	0L	$0 \, m^3$	$0 \, m^3$

Conclusion

Dipsticks 1 and 2 are for a cuboid tank, dipstick 3 is for a conical tank and dipsticks 4 and 5 are for the cylindrical tank.

All of these dipsticks are about 5 cm from the bottom to the top mark so real dipsticks would have to be scaled for the container.

Checklist for the AO1 task

Higher tier

☐ Have you explained each step of your work, and made it clear why you have altered your approach?

☐ Is your mathematics of a sufficient standard and are your results accurate?

☐ Is your algebra accurate and done correctly, e.g. brackets used where necessary?

☐ Is all the mathematics you have used relevant to the problem?

☐ Have you proved your results using at least two different methods, e.g. numerically, algebraically or by considering spatial aspects?

☐ Have you used commentary to link together the different methods?

The *Handling Data* task – AO4

How the AO4 task is marked

Strand one is called *Specify and plan*. This strand is about how you plan your project, what type of data you will collect and how you will analyse it.

Strand two is called *Collect, process and represent*. This strand is about how you collect and show your data and the statistical techniques you use to choose your sample.

Strand three is called *Interpret and discuss*. This strand is about the conclusions you draw from your data and how this relates to the statistical measures, diagrams, charts and tables you have produced.

The following table outlines what you should do for each mark for Strand two. This doesn't mean that drawing a pie chart automatically gets you a mark of 3 but it is a rough guide to the types of mathematics you should be using.

Mark	Collecting	Representing	Processing
1	Use lists to collect discrete data Use a frequency table to collect discrete data	Bar Charts Pictograms	Mode of discrete data Range
2	Grouped data in equal class intervals	Frequency diagrams for discrete data Line graphs Modal group	Mode of grouped data
3	Use lists to collect discrete data for two separate but related distributions	Simple pie charts Stem and leaf diagrams	Reading pie charts Mean and median of discrete data
4	Collect and record continuous data, choosing appropriate class intervals	More difficult pie charts Frequency diagrams for continuous data Scatter diagrams	Correlation
5	Collect and record data relevant to the hypothesis	Frequency polygons	Mean, modal class and median of grouped data Line of best fit on a scatter diagram
6	Collect and record data relevant to the hypothesis that is reliable and takes into account any bias that might have arisen from the method of collection	Cumulative frequency diagrams Box plots Time series graphs	Median and interquartile range from cumulative frequency diagrams Moving averages
7	Data collection recognises problems that may be encountered such as non-response and reliability	Histograms	Medians from histograms Comparison of histograms
8	All data collected is relevant; there is no unnecessary data. The data takes account of any bias that might have been met in collecting it		Correlation coefficients Standard Deviation Skewness Rank correlation (see page 45)

General advice for approaching the AO4 task

You can collect the data yourself (this is called *primary data*) or you can download it from the internet or a database (this is called *secondary data*).

It is important that you choose a suitable sample and use a suitable *sample size*. You need to collect at least 30 sets of data and each set must have at least *two aspects* to it. You must also decide how you intend to collect your data and what type of *sampling method* you will use, e.g. *random sampling, stratified sampling, quota sampling,* etc.

It is important that you state a *hypothesis*. This is the idea that you will try to analyse in your project. You must have at least one hypothesis, but it is better to have more. To get higher marks you need further hypotheses that extend the original hypothesis and take your statistical analysis into a new, but related, area.

You must give a well-structured plan of how you intend to carry out the task. If possible you should explain how you intend to avoid *bias* when collecting your data. This is vital for the higher marks.

Any comment on your data, relevant or not, gets you a mark of 1. However, for a mark of 8 you need to make very detailed and correct inferences from your data.

You need to refer back to your original hypothesis and you must give a clear explanation of how you have investigated it. You must comment on whether your analysis has supported your hypothesis or not.

You should also summarise what you have done and make a comment on how you might have improved your analysis, referring to any bias in your sample and ways that you have tried to eliminate it.

You may produce further hypotheses as the work progresses.

Types of data

There are two types of data, *qualitative* and *quantitative*.
Qualitative data is data such as colour of eyes, make of car, etc.
Quantitative data is numerical data, and can be separated into *discrete* and *continuous* data. Discrete data involves counting and is data such as the number of people in a family, marks in an exam, etc. Continuous data involves measuring and is data that takes a range of values such as height or speed of cars. You may not get the higher marks if you only use qualitative or discrete data.

You could do a series of the body measurements for the members of your class. You could collect data for gender, eye colour, height, weight, arm span, head circumference, shoe size, distance from nose to navel, etc. This would be a mixture of qualitative data (gender, eye colour), discrete quantitative data (shoe size) and continuous quantitative data (arm span). This is primary data and you would need to design and use a *data collection sheet*.

You could collect information about word lengths in newspapers and magazines and compare them. You would need to have articles with over 100 words and the two aspects could be articles on the same topic from two clearly different types of magazines or newspapers. This would be discrete quantitative data.

You could download some football results from a web-site for a couple of football clubs and compare them. This would be secondary data.

You could look at the examination results for the SATs tests for English, Maths and Science. Your school will have these on a database. This would be secondary discrete quantitative data.

You could do a memory game seeing how many objects people remember. You would need at least 30 people and the two aspects could be the gender of the person and/or their age.

Foundation tier

Advice for Foundation tier

- Start by deciding on your hypothesis (the topic you want to find out about).

- Decide what data you will need and how you will collect it.

- Plan how you will analyse your data so that you can interpret it and form a conclusion.

- Use this diagram of the **Data Handling Cycle** to help you plan.

Data Handling Cycle

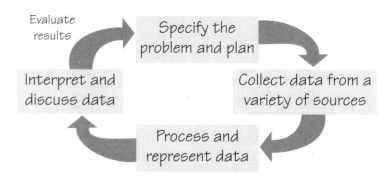

AO4 Criteria for marks of 3 and 4

To get a 1/3 you need to cover each of the following bullet points. To get 1/4 you need to cover all the following bullet points *and* at least one bullet point (but not all) from A04 1/5 or 1/6 on page 36. This is the same for Strands two and three – to get a mark of 4 you must cover at least one bullet point (but not all) shown for marks 5 and 6 on pages 36–7. **What this means**

AO4 1/3 and 1/4

Candidates choose a problem involving routine use of simple statistical techniques and set out reasonably clear aims. Consideration is given to the collection of data. Candidates describe an overall plan largely designed to meet the aims of and structure the project report so that results relating to some of the aims are brought out. Where appropriate, they use a sample of adequate size.

- You choose a project that allows you to investigate a simple hypothesis. You should state your hypothesis at the beginning of your report.
- Your plan, which should be stated at the beginning of the report, allows you to investigate your hypothesis.
- Your sample is appropriate for investigating the hypothesis and large enough to give you reliable results (e.g. larger than 30).

AO4 2/3 and 2/4

Candidates collect data with some relevance to the problem and plan. The data are collected or recorded with some consideration given to efficient processing. Candidates use straightforward and largely relevant calculations involving techniques

- You collect data that is relevant to the problem.
- You represent this data using, for example, pie charts, frequency diagrams, stem and leaf diagrams, line graphs or scatter diagrams.
- You process the data by using, for example, the mode, mean, median (of discrete data) or correlation.
- Your calculations and diagrams are generally correct.

of at least the level detailed in the handling data paragraph of the grade description for grade F. The results are generally correct. Candidates show understanding of situations by describing them using statistical concepts, words and diagrams. They synthesise information presented in a variety of forms. Their writing explains and informs their use of diagrams, which are usually related to their overall plan. They present their diagrams correctly, with suitable scales and titles.

A04 3/3 and 3/4

Candidates comment on patterns in the data and any exceptions. They summarise and give a reasonably correct interpretation of their graphs and calculations. They attempt to relate the summarised data to the initial problem, though some conclusions may be incorrect or irrelevant. They make some attempt to evaluate their strategy.

- You make comments about representations of the data you have collected using the statistics (such as mode, mean, etc.) that you have calculated.
- Your comments need to be relevant to your original hypothesis.

Cars

The following task gets a mark of 4 in each strand.

Davina's answer

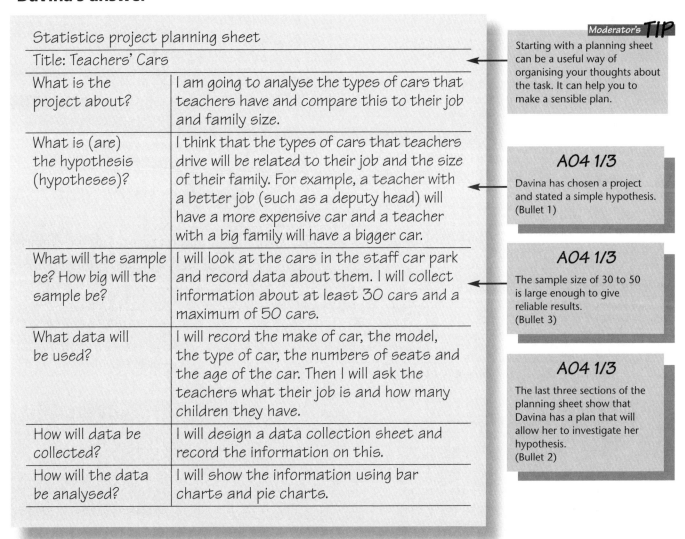

Statistics project planning sheet

Title: Teachers' Cars

What is the project about?	I am going to analyse the types of cars that teachers have and compare this to their job and family size.
What is (are) the hypothesis (hypotheses)?	I think that the types of cars that teachers drive will be related to their job and the size of their family. For example, a teacher with a better job (such as a deputy head) will have a more expensive car and a teacher with a big family will have a bigger car.
What will the sample be? How big will the sample be?	I will look at the cars in the staff car park and record data about them. I will collect information about at least 30 cars and a maximum of 50 cars.
What data will be used?	I will record the make of car, the model, the type of car, the numbers of seats and the age of the car. Then I will ask the teachers what their job is and how many children they have.
How will data be collected?	I will design a data collection sheet and record the information on this.
How will the data be analysed?	I will show the information using bar charts and pie charts.

Moderator's TIP

Starting with a planning sheet can be a useful way of organising your thoughts about the task. It can help you to make a sensible plan.

A04 1/3

Davina has chosen a project and stated a simple hypothesis. (Bullet 1)

A04 1/3

The sample size of 30 to 50 is large enough to give reliable results. (Bullet 3)

A04 1/3

The last three sections of the planning sheet show that Davina has a plan that will allow her to investigate her hypothesis. (Bullet 2)

Hypothesis 1: Teachers with bigger families will have bigger cars.

Hypothesis 2: Teachers with better jobs will have more expensive cars.

Collecting data

This is the data I have collected. I went round the staff and asked them if they minded me recording some information about their cars. If they agreed I asked them how many children they had, got the registration number then went into the car park (with the Head's permission!) and recorded the data.

The age of the car can be worked out from the number plate. I have rounded this to the nearest year to make calculations easier.

The job information came from the school handbook. I found out that teachers get scale points but the school handbook doesn't give that information so I allocated a number from 1 to 6 for the type of job. For example, a new teacher without a special job in school would be a 1 and the Head and Deputies would be a 6.

Car	Make	Model	Type	No of seats	Age of car	Teacher's job	Number of children
1	Ford	Ka	Saloon	4	2 yrs	2	2
2	Vauxhall	Vectra	Hatchback	5	4 yrs	4	1
3	Mitzubishi	Shogun	4 x 4	5	3 yrs	5	3
4	Toyota	MR2	Sports	2	3 yrs	2	0
5	Ford	Sierra	Saloon	5	5 yrs	1	2
6	VW	Bora	Saloon	5	2 yrs	3	3
7	Vauxhall	Zafira	People carrier	7	2 yrs	2	2
8	Ford	Galaxy	People carrier	6	4 yrs	6	0
9	MG	MGB	Sports	2	9 yrs	3	4
10	Suzuki	Swift	Saloon	4	6 yrs	1	0
⋮	⋮	⋮	⋮	⋮	⋮	⋮	⋮
49	Renault	Clio	Saloon	4	4 yrs	1	1
50	Nissan	Primera	Hatchback	5	2 yrs	2	2

<u>What the data shows</u>

This is a pie chart showing the types of cars that teachers have.

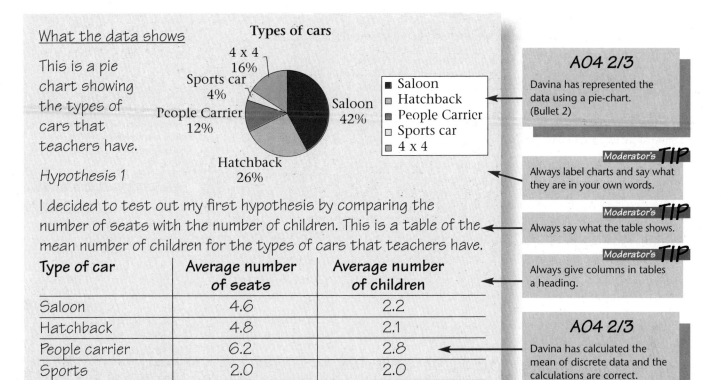

Types of cars

4 x 4 16%
Sports car 4%
People Carrier 12%
Saloon 42%
Hatchback 26%

- ■ Saloon
- ▨ Hatchback
- ▨ People Carrier
- □ Sports car
- ▨ 4 x 4

A04 2/3

Davina has represented the data using a pie-chart. (Bullet 2)

Moderator's **TIP**
Always label charts and say what they are in your own words.

Hypothesis 1

I decided to test out my first hypothesis by comparing the number of seats with the number of children. This is a table of the mean number of children for the types of cars that teachers have.

Moderator's **TIP**
Always say what the table shows.

Moderator's **TIP**
Always give columns in tables a heading.

Type of car	Average number of seats	Average number of children
Saloon	4.6	2.2
Hatchback	4.8	2.1
People carrier	6.2	2.8
Sports	2.0	2.0
4 x 4	5.2	2.2

A04 2/3

Davina has calculated the mean of discrete data and the calculations are correct. (Bullets 3 and 4)

This doesn't really prove my hypothesis but some of the teachers buy cars for different reasons other than carrying children about. One teacher with a people carrier hasn't got any children but goes camping in France in the summer, and of the two teachers who own sports cars, one is an older teacher with four kids who have all left home, and the other is a young teacher who isn't married.

A04 3/3

Davina makes a comment about her data using information from the table that she has calculated. (Bullet 1)

Hypothesis 2

I will now look at my second hypothesis by looking at the ages of the cars and the jobs of the teachers. This is a graph showing the teacher's job scale against the age of their car.

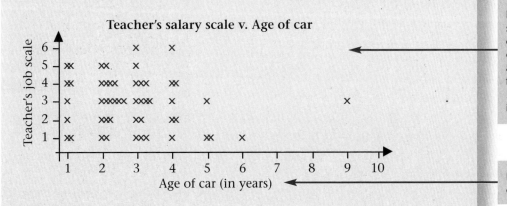

Teacher's salary scale v. Age of car

Teacher's job scale (y-axis): 1 to 6
Age of car (in years) (x-axis): 1 to 10

A04 2/4

Davina has used a type of scatter graph to compare her data. The calculations are correct. These are the second and third bullets from the list for A04 2/5 and 2/6 on page 36 so Davina gets a mark of 4 in Strand two.

Moderator's **TIP**
Make sure your graph axes are correctly labelled.

This graph doesn't show anything, so I worked out the average age of the car for each level of job.

This table shows the results.

Job	1	2	3	4	5	6
Average age of car	3.2	2.6	3.1	2.7	1.8	3.5

There is a slight trend that teachers with better jobs have younger cars.

The 9-year-old car throws out the mean for the teachers on level 3, and the Heads and Deputies don't follow the trend either. The 9-year-old car is a 'classic' according to the teacher who owns it and the Head and Deputies have quite expensive cars even if they are a couple of years old.

I decided to look at the comparison another way.

I found out the costs of the different makes of cars when new, using a car trading magazine.

This is a graph showing the teacher's job against the cost of the type of car (when new).

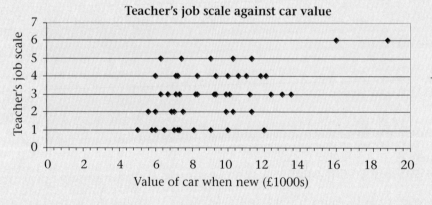

This shows a bit more of a trend but probably isn't realistic as the cars may have been bought second-hand anyway.

Conclusion

I don't think that either of my hypotheses is true. Some people buy big cars because they have families. Some families have two cars anyway so this data isn't comprehensive. The teachers in my school are probably representative of a certain area of the population as a whole and when I look round my friends' families they have a variety of cars even though some are big families.

A04 3/3

The comments Davina makes about her analysis are relevant to her original hypothesis. (Bullet 2)

Moderator's **TIP**

Cost of cars is discrete data but it can be analysed like continuous data. You need to use continuous data to get higher marks.

Moderator's **TIP**

Costs of cars is continuous quantitative data because they can take any value in a range of values.

A04 3/4

Throughout the task Davina has made comments about the data she has collected. She has used means to compare the data and a scatter graph to represent it. She has related her conclusions to the data and to her original hypotheses.

Moderator's **TIP**

It is not necessary to prove that your original hypotheses were correct. However, to move to higher marks Davina should look in more detail at the reasons why her data may not be valid.

Moderator's **TIP**

Always write a conclusion. This must be about the original hypothesis.

A04 3/4

The comments in the conclusion cover bullets one and three from the list for A04 3/5 and 3/6 on page 37, so Davina gets a mark of 4 in Strand three.

How to get the next mark up

The task above gets a mark of 4 in each strand. If Davina wanted to get a higher mark than 4 she would need to investigate her hypotheses further. As a better way of assessing the value of the car, she could look at their values after two years as a percentage of the original cost or look at how the petrol consumption varies with the engine size. She would need to use more advanced statistical techniques such as means of grouped data or scatter graphs. She would also need to do some comparisons of her data.

Checklist for the AO4 task
Foundation tier

Planning

☐ Have you stated the aim of your task at the beginning?

☐ Have you stated your hypothesis (what you want to find out)?

☐ Have you written out a plan covering the following?
   – What information you will need.
   – How you will collect the information.

☐ Do you need to design a questionnaire?

☐ Is your sample large enough?

Processing

☐ Is your data relevant to the problem?

☐ How will you process the data?

☐ Have you checked that your calculations are correct?

☐ Have you chosen suitable diagrams and explained them?

Interpreting

☐ Have you written down all your results?

☐ Have you written down all the ideas that you have had and justified them with reference to your calculations or diagrams?

☐ Have you referred your results back to the original hypothesis?

☐ Have you considered what more you could do to give better, more reliable results?

☐ Have you written a conclusion that relates to your original hypothesis?

Intermediate tier

Advice for intermediate tier

- Choose a problem to investigate that will give you enough scope to examine it in depth.

- State your aims clearly at the start of your report.

- Decide what data you need, how you will collect it, and what size your sample will be.

- Use this diagram of the **Data Handling Cycle** to help you plan.

Data Handling Cycle

State the hypothesis you are going to test → Collect relevant data using a suitably sized sample → Process and represent data → Analyse your data suggesting reasons for any exceptions → Write a conclusion → State the hypothesis you are going to test

AO4 Criteria for marks of 5 and 6

To get 1/5 you need to cover each of the following bullet points for Strand one. To get 1/6 you need to cover all the following bullet points *and* at least one bullet point (but not all) from A04 1/7 and 1/8 on page 46. This is the same for Strands two and three – to get a mark of 6 you must cover at least one bullet point (but not all) shown for marks 7 and 8 on pages 46–7.

What this means

AO4 1/5 and 1/6

Candidates consider a more complex problem. They choose appropriate data to collect and state their aims in statistical terms with the selection of an appropriate plan. Their plan is designed to meet the aims and is well-described. Candidates consider the practical problems of carrying out the survey or experiment. Where appropriate, they give reasons for choosing a particular sampling method. The project report is well structured so that the project can be seen as a whole.

- You choose an area that allows you to investigate your original hypothesis in depth and you state further hypotheses. You state your aims clearly at the beginning of the report.
- Your plan, which should also be stated at the beginning of your report, is clear and designed to meet the aims.
- You choose an appropriate sample, in both size (at least 30) and variety, and give reasons for your choice of sample, taking variability and bias into account.

AO4 2/5 and 2/6

Candidates collect largely relevant and mainly reliable data. The data are collected in a form designed to ensure that they can be used. Candidates use a range of more demanding, largely relevant calculations that include techniques of at least the level detailed in the handling data paragraph of the grade description for grade C. The results are generally correct and no obviously relevant calculation is omitted. There is little redundancy in calculation or presentation. Candidates convey statistical meaning through precise and consistent use of statistical concepts that is sustained throughout the work. They use appropriate diagrams for representing data and give a reason for their choice of presentation, explaining features they have selected.

- You collect data that is relevant to the problem.
- You represent this data using frequency polygons, cumulative frequency diagrams, box plots and/or time series graphs.
- You analyse the data using techniques such as mean, mode and median of grouped data, interquartile range, lines of best fit on scatter diagrams, or moving averages.
- Your calculations and diagrams should be correct.
- There should not be any calculations that are not relevant, i.e. you will lose marks if you just give lots of different representations or calculations that don't help in supporting or rejecting your hypothesis.

A04 3/5 and 3/6

Candidates comment on patterns in the data and suggest reasons for exceptions. They summarise and correctly interpret their graphs and calculations, relate the summarised data to the initial problem and draw appropriate inferences. Candidates use summary statistics to make relevant comparisons and show an informal appreciation that results may not be statistically significant. Where relevant, they allow for the nature of the sampling method in making inferences about the population. They evaluate the effectiveness of the overall strategy and make a simple assessment of limitations.

- You make a comment summarising the results from the data you have collected.
- You comment on your data using the statistics, such as the interquartile range or moving averages, that you have calculated.
- Your comments need to link back and be relevant to the original hypothesis.
- You consider what you have done and make suggestions for further progress or criticise your results.
- You correctly interpret your diagrams such as box plots.

Weather

The following task gets a mark of 6 in each strand.

Ben's answer

I did a search on the Internet for 'weather data uk' and I found a website that gave a lot of data about the weather and other conditions at the Fair Isle weather station. There was a lot of data I could have investigated. However, I decided to focus on just a few areas.

I have decided to record the mean maximum temperature (in °C), the mean minimum temperature (in °C), the mean sea temperature (in °C), the total rainfall (in mm), the total sunshine (in hours), the mean wind speed (in kilometres per hour), and the percentage of wind direction for the main points of the compass.

This is my data which I cut and pasted into an EXCEL spreadsheet.

Month	Max temp (°C)	Min temp (°C)	Sea temp (°C)	Rain (mm)	Total sun (hrs)	Mean wind speed (kph)	% wind N	% wind NE	% wind E	% wind SE	% wind S	% wind SW	% wind W	% wind NW	Calm
Aug–95	14.9	11.0	12.0	25.3	160.0	10.1	19.4	3.2	3.2	19.4	12.9	25.8	6.5	9.7	–0.1
Sep–95	13.0	9.9	12.1	131.0	99.1	15.1	16.7	10.0	23.3	10.0	3.3	10.0	13.3	10.0	3.4
Oct–95	11.9	8.7	11.3	96.8	92.3	19.0	0.0	0.0	3.2	16.1	41.9	16.1	16.1	6.5	0.1
Nov–95	8.8	6.3	10.8	68.8	36.3	15.4	13.3	3.3	13.3	13.3	16.7	10.0	20.0	6.7	3.4
Dec–95	5.0	2.6	8.7	51.1	26.4	16.4	25.8	12.9	12.9	16.1	9.7	3.2	9.7	6.5	3.2
Jan–96	6.5	4.9	7.7	27.5	16.3	21.7	0.0	3.2	12.9	58.1	22.6	3.2	0.0	0.0	0.0
Feb–96	4.8	2.1	6.6	70.7	53.2	20.5	13.8	3.4	10.3	13.8	17.2	20.7	13.8	6.9	0.1
Oct–99	10.9	8.2	11.5	131.0	58.4	17.1	6.5	3.2	16.1	16.1	9.7	16.1	25.8	6.5	0.0
Nov–99	9.1	6.5	10.6	119.0	25.9	18.6	16.7	0.0	0.0	13.3	23.3	36.7	10.0	0.0	0.0
Dec–99	5.6	2.7	9.0	184.0	15.3	19.6	16.1	6.5	0.0	6.5	12.9	16.1	22.6	19.4	–0.1

The first thing I did was check through the data to see if it made sense. The 'CALM' figures for March 1997 did not seem correct.

A04 1/5

Ben gives some thought to the sample and decides to focus on a small subset of the data. (Bullet 3)

A04 2/5

The data collected is relevant to the implied plan. You should show all data collected either in the main report or as an appendix as it will need to be checked for accuracy. (Bullet 1)

Moderator's **TIP**

You should always show all the data you have collected. It is not displayed here for reasons of space.

Moderator's **TIP**

You should always check data as it is easy to mistype or record data incorrectly. If you find incorrect data collect it again. In this case, Ben uses historical data to alter the figures.

I used this formula to calculate the CALM figures.

CALM = −10.8 = 100 − (N + NE + E + SE + S + SW + W + NW)

It doesn't seem reasonable to have such a large negative percentage of calm days. First I checked that the numbers were correct, which they were. I then compared the data for the month with the historical data listed alongside.

March 1997

% wind direction	N	NE	E	SE	S	SW	W	NW	Calm
March 1997	10.7	3.6	7.1	14.3	17.9	35.7	17.9	3.6	−10.8
Mean for each March 1974–94	10.2	4.8	8.2	15.5	17.4	18.4	14.4	10.5	0.6

Most of the data for March 1997 compares with that for the averages from 1974–1994 except for SW which is very different. I suspect that the value was supposed to be 25.7 and was entered wrongly. I changed this in the data set.

Now I have got all the data I will have to decide what to analyse.

Hypothesis 1

The temperature patterns are the same each year.

To investigate this hypothesis I will draw line graphs of the temperature for the years 1996, 1997, 1998 and 1999. (There isn't a whole year's worth of data for 1995). These graphs should have approximately the same shape.

Hypothesis 2

Total monthly rainfall and sea-water temperature are related.

To investigate this hypothesis I will compare the water temperature and the rainfall on a scatter graph. If my hypothesis is correct there should be a negative correlation as I expect there to be a higher water temperature in the summer when the rainfall is least.

Hypothesis 3

The mean wind speed is related to the mean wind direction.

To investigate this hypothesis I will work out a way of finding the main wind direction for each month and then plot this against the mean wind speed. If my hypothesis is correct there should be a correlation.

A04 1/5

Ben considers the accuracy of the data, considering any biased data.
(Bullet 3)

A04 2/5

Consideration is given to the accuracy of the data and the processing of the data. All calculations are correct.
(Bullet 4)

Moderator's TIP

At this point Ben starts his investigation by giving a plan and hypotheses. Before he was just discussing the data.

A04 1/5

Ben gets to his plan and hypotheses. The comments about data collection above mean that the data chosen will enable Ben to investigate his hypotheses.
(Bullet 2)

Moderator's TIP

State a clear hypothesis and give a simple plan of what you are going to do and what you expect to happen.

A04 1/5

The hypotheses chosen allow Ben to investigate the data in different areas. The way he will carry out his investigation is explained.
(Bullet 1)

Hypothesis 4

The average temperature of the sea is increasing due to global warming.

To investigate this hypothesis I will work out a three-point moving average for the sea temperature. If my hypothesis is correct this will fluctuate but will show an upward trend.

Hypothesis 1 – Temperature

The graphs below show the mean maximum temperature each month plotted for 12 months for the years 1996 to 1999.

Mean daily temperatures

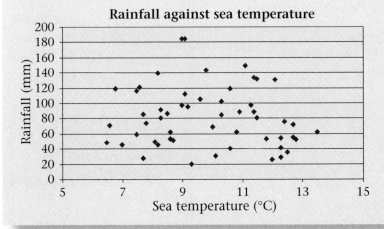

> ### A04 2/5
> Ben uses a time series graph to compare the mean monthly temperatures for four years. (Bullet 2)

This clearly shows that my first hypothesis was correct. The trend of the average daily temperatures is very similar for all four years surveyed.

> ### A04 3/5
> Ben makes a comment summarising some of the data he has analysed. (Bullet 1)

Hypothesis 2 – Rainfall and sea temperature

Below is a scatter graph of rainfall against sea temperature. It looks as though there is no correlation. The product moment correlation coefficient (see appendix) is –0.11, which means that there is a very slight negative correlation but basically there is no relationship between sea temperature and rainfall. This means that my second hypothesis is wrong.

> ### Moderator's TIP
> When you use mathematics that is beyond the GCSE syllabus you should define it (see pages 44–5).

Rainfall against sea temperature

> ### A04 2/5
> Ben uses a scatter graph with a relevant comment. Product moment correlation coefficient is beyond the GCSE specification but just using it to back up what is obvious from the scatter graph will not get higher marks. It must be used in an appropriate way. (Bullet 3)

Hypothesis 3 – Mean wind speed and direction

I need to decide how to calculate a mean wind direction. I am going to do this by calculating the mean angle of the wind using a bearing.

To calculate the mean angle of the wind direction I will multiply the percentage in each direction with the equivalent bearing and divide by 100. This is like a weighted average.

Example – August 1995

This is the normal compass rose with bearings marked on.	This is the percentage of wind in the compass directions.	This is the mean angle.

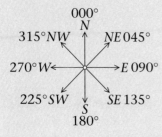 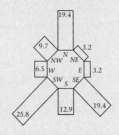 

This was calculated by doing

$$\frac{0 \times 19.4 + 45 \times 3.2 + 90 \times 3.2 + 135 \times 19.4 + 180 \times 12.9 + 225 \times 25.8 + 270 \times 6.5 + 315 \times 9.7}{100}$$

$$= \frac{15988.5}{100}$$

$$= 160 \ (2 \ \text{s.f.})$$

I actually used the spreadsheet to calculate these. ◄—

I have calculated the mean angle of the wind direction for each month and plotted this against the mean wind speed. This is the scatter graph.

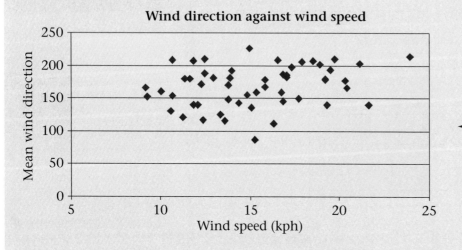

The product moment correlation coefficient is 0.28 which shows a slight positive correlation.

The scatter graph does not prove my third hypothesis, so I have to conclude that the wind speed is not dependent on the wind direction.

Moderator's **TIP**

It doesn't matter if your hypothesis was wrong. As long as have you done a valid analysis you will still get full credit for your work.

Hypothesis 4 – Global warming

The following is the graph of the sea temperature for the 53 months that the data covers, starting with August 1995.

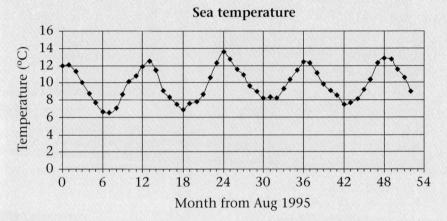

This graph shows the same fluctuations as the mean sea temperature but over four and a half years. The data needs to be smoothed out. I will do this by taking a 12-point moving average. I decided to do a 12-point moving average as a 3-point average still had the same fluctuations but a 12-point moving average would take all seasons into account.

Moderator's **TIP**

This is a change of plan. You can change your plan if you explain why you are doing so.

A04 3/5

Ben considers his idea to use a three point moving average and realises that it won't work. So he suggests a twelve point moving average to make further progress.
(Bullet 4)

The first 12-point moving average was calculated using the first 12 months' values for sea temperature and finding their mean.

$$\frac{12 + 12.1 + 11.3 + 10.8 + 8.7 + 7.7 + 6.6 + 6.5 + 7 + 8.6 + 10.1 + 10.8}{12}$$

$$= \frac{111.4}{12}$$

$$= 9.28 \text{ (2 d.p.)}$$

I actually used the spreadsheet to work these out.

Moderator's **TIP**

Once again show the mathematical formula in your spreadsheet as an appendix.

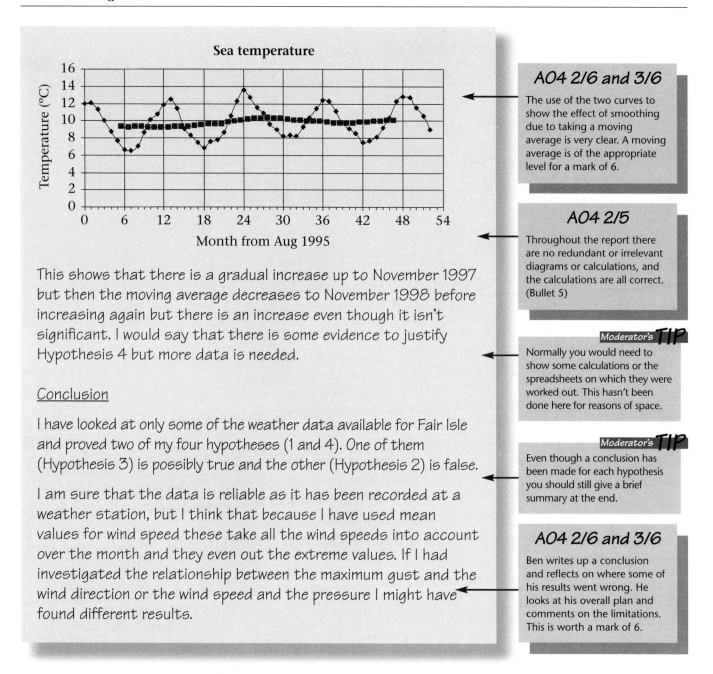

Sea temperature

This shows that there is a gradual increase up to November 1997 but then the moving average decreases to November 1998 before increasing again but there is an increase even though it isn't significant. I would say that there is some evidence to justify Hypothesis 4 but more data is needed.

Conclusion

I have looked at only some of the weather data available for Fair Isle and proved two of my four hypotheses (1 and 4). One of them (Hypothesis 3) is possibly true and the other (Hypothesis 2) is false.

I am sure that the data is reliable as it has been recorded at a weather station, but I think that because I have used mean values for wind speed these take all the wind speeds into account over the month and they even out the extreme values. If I had investigated the relationship between the maximum gust and the wind direction or the wind speed and the pressure I might have found different results.

A04 2/6 and 3/6

The use of the two curves to show the effect of smoothing due to taking a moving average is very clear. A moving average is of the appropriate level for a mark of 6.

A04 2/5

Throughout the report there are no redundant or irrelevant diagrams or calculations, and the calculations are all correct. (Bullet 5)

Moderator's TIP

Normally you would need to show some calculations or the spreadsheets on which they were worked out. This hasn't been done here for reasons of space.

Moderator's TIP

Even though a conclusion has been made for each hypothesis you should still give a brief summary at the end.

A04 2/6 and 3/6

Ben writes up a conclusion and reflects on where some of his results went wrong. He looks at his overall plan and comments on the limitations. This is worth a mark of 6.

A04 1/6

Ben has covered all the bullet points for A04 1/5 and 1/6. The project is sufficiently demanding to allow use of more advanced techniques. This is bullet 1 from the list for A04 1/7 and 1/8, so Ben gets a mark of 6 in Strand one.

A04 2/6

Ben has covered all the bullets for A04 2/5 and 2/6. There are no irrelevant calculations or diagrams. Also the explanation and conclusion link back to the original hypothesis. These are bullets 5 and 6 from the list for A04 2/7 and 2/8 on page 46, so Ben gets a mark of 6 in Strand two.

A04 3/6

Ben has covered all the bullets for A04 3/5 and 3/6. Ben considers in his conclusion how the analysis could be improved. This is bullet 4 from the list for A04 3/7 and 3/8 on page 47, so Ben gets a mark of 6 in Strand three.

How to get the next mark up

Ben has some ideas that might take the work to a mark of 7, but to do this he would need to use higher level techniques. The nature of the data is restrictive. Ben could group the data, draw histograms and calculate interquartile ranges but these would not really make the problem more substantial.

Checklist for the AO4 task

Unlike the AO1 task, which often starts with a simple task that can be moved to the higher marks by developing as the task progresses, most of the planning for the AO4 task needs to be done at the beginning.

Intermediate tier

Planning

☐ Have you chosen a suitable problem that you will be able to investigate in depth?

☐ Have you written a clear plan designed to meet your aims?

☐ Have you decided what data you need and how you will collect it? Is your sample suitable in size and variety?

☐ If you have used a questionnaire, have you included a copy and are the questions relevant and unbiased?

Processing

☐ Have you extended at least one area of the original problem to give further hypotheses?

☐ Is your raw data presented in an understandable way, e.g. in a grouped table, or a spreadsheet?

☐ Have you used techniques such as mean, median and mode of grouped data, interquartile range, line of best fit on scatter graphs, and moving averages to analyse your data?

☐ Have you used a spreadsheet to analyse your data? (This way you can be sure that your calculations are accurate.)

Interpreting

☐ Have you summarised your results?

☐ Have you made comparisons between your sets of data using statistics such as the interquartile range and moving averages?

☐ Have you referred your results back to the original hypothesis?

☐ Have you considered the limitations of your results and how this may affect your conclusions?

☐ Have you considered what more you could do to give better, more reliable results?

☐ Have you evaluated your strategy? (This is not just a conclusion but you should consider whether your methods allowed you to investigate your hypothesis effectively.)

Higher tier
Advice for Higher tier

- Choose a problem that is difficult enough for you to be able to use more advanced statistical techniques.

- State your aims and the plan you intend to use to achieve your aims, giving reasons.

- Say what data you intend to collect, how you will deal with any problems in collecting it and how you will avoid bias.

- Interpret and summarise your results and make inferences from them with reference to your hypothesis.

- Use this diagram of the **Data Handling Cycle** to help you plan your work.

Data Handling Cycle

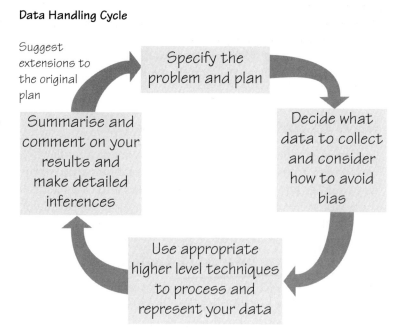

Other ways of processing data

The following statistical measures are beyond the Handling Data section of the GCSE specification but they may be useful when analysing data at the higher marks. It is not necessary to use these measures to get the highest marks. If they are used you must show that you understand what they do and they must be interpreted correctly.

Standard deviation

This is a measure of spread, centred on the mean. Inter-quartile range is another measure of spread, centred on the median. The inter-quartile range eliminates extreme values whilst the standard deviation uses all the data.

The formula for standard deviation for a set of discrete data is:

$$S.D. = \sqrt{\frac{\sum x^2}{n} - \bar{x}^2} \quad \text{or} \quad \sqrt{\frac{\sum (x - \bar{x})^2}{n}}$$

The formula for standard deviation for a frequency table is:

$$S.D. = \sqrt{\frac{\sum fx^2}{n} - \bar{x}^2} \quad \text{or} \quad \sqrt{\frac{\sum f(x - \bar{x})^2}{n}}$$

Standard deviation can be calculated using the above formulae but it can easily be done automatically by graphical calculators or on spreadsheets. [Please note that Standard Deviation is in the Welsh National Curriculum, so will not be considered outside GCSE Curriculum by Exam boards for Welsh Exams.]

Product moment correlation coefficient (PMCC).

This is a measure of how good the relationship between two sets of data is. You would use this with a scatter diagram.

If the PMCC is 1 then the data has perfect positive correlation.
If the PMCC is –1 then the data has perfect negative correlation.

It is unlikely that your data will be perfectly related but the nearer the value of the PMCC is to 1 or –1, the better the relationship. A PMCC near to zero means that there is no correlation.

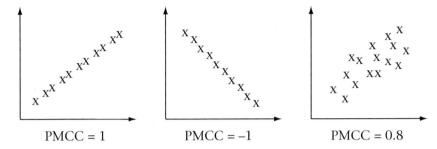

PMCC = 1   PMCC = –1   PMCC = 0.8

Skewness

This is a measure of how spread the data is on either side of the mean. A value of zero means the distribution is symmetrical. A negative value means the data is skewed below the mean and a positive value means the data is skewed above the mean. The higher the numerical value, the greater the skewness.

These statistical measures are not easy to calculate as they require complicated tables of data. It is easy to make errors. However, you will not gain any marks for being able to calculate these statistical measures. You will only gain marks for using them in an appropriate way. This is why it is better to use a computer, in particular, a spreadsheet, to process your data.

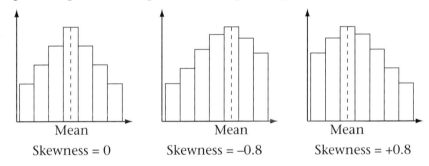

Mean   Mean   Mean

Skewness = 0   Skewness = –0.8   Skewness = +0.8

Rank Correlation

This is way of comparing two lists of data. For example, if two people are asked to rank 10 TV programmes in order of preference, they may get a table of data such as:

Programme	A	B	C	D	E	F	G	H	I	J
Person A	7	5	3	1	8	4	2	9	10	6
Person B	6	4	2	3	7	1	5	10	9	8
Difference	1	1	1	2	1	3	3	1	1	2

To calculate the rank correlation, s, calculate the difference, d, between the ranks and use the formula:

$S = 1 - \dfrac{6\sum d^2}{n(n^2 - 1)}$, where $\sum d^2$ is the sum of the square of each difference and n is the number of categories to rank (in this case 10).

A04 Criteria for marks of 7 and 8

To get a 1/7 you need to cover each of the following bullet points.
To get 1/8 you need to cover all the bullet points and consider any problems, such as bias, with your data and take steps to overcome these problems.

What this means

A04 1/7 and 1/8

Candidates work on a problem requiring creative thinking and careful specification. They state their aims clearly in statistical terms and develop an appropriate plan to meet these aims giving reasons for their choice. They foresee and plan for practical problems in carrying out the survey or experiment. Where appropriate, they consider the nature and size of sample to be used and take steps to avoid bias. Where appropriate, they use techniques such as control groups, or pre-tests or questionnaires or data sheets, and refine these to enhance the project. The project report is well structured and the conclusions are well related to the initial aims.

- You should choose a more demanding project so that you can use more advanced statistical techniques.
- You state your aims about using the advanced techniques clearly and give valid reasons for your new plan. This can be stated later in the report as your project develops.
- You explain any limitations (for example, bias) that may arise from your chosen sample and change your plan based on this.
- During the project you might refine your questionnaire or method of collecting data in the light of your findings so far.

To get a 2/7 you need to cover each of the following bullet points.
To get 2/8 you need to cover each of the bullet points and use some more advanced statistical techniques to collect, process and represent your data.

A04 2/7 and 2/8

Candidates collect reliable data relevant to the problem under consideration. They deal with practical problems such as non-response, missing data, or ensuring secondary data are appropriate. Candidates use a range of relevant calculations that include techniques of at least the level detailed in the data handling paragraph of the grade description for grade A. These calculations are correct and no obviously relevant calculation is omitted. Numerical results are rounded appropriately. There is no redundancy in calculation or presentation. Candidates use language and statistical concepts effectively in presenting a convincing reasoned argument. They use an appropriate range of diagrams to summarise the data and show how variables are related.

- You collect data that is relevant to the problem and takes variability and bias into account.
- You consider the limitations on your data.
- You represent and analyse this data using histograms, for example.
- You analyse the data using techniques such as standard deviation, product moment correlation coefficient, skewness and other techniques.
- Your calculations and diagrams are correct and there are no irrelevant calculations and diagrams.
- Your explanation links all the diagrams and calculations together and relates back to the original problem.

To get 3/7 you need to cover each of the following bullet points.
To get 3/8 you need to cover all the bullet points and consider the limitations of your analysis and act upon them.

A04 3/7 and 3/8

Candidates comment on patterns and give plausible reasons for exceptions. They correctly summarise and interpret graphs and calculations. They make correct and detailed inferences from the data concerning the original problem using the vocabulary of probability. Candidates appreciate the significance of results they obtain. Where relevant, they allow for the nature and size of the sample and any possible bias in making inferences about the population. They evaluate the effectiveness of the overall strategy and recognise limitations of the work done, making suggestions for improvement. They comment constructively on the practical consequences of the work.

- You make comments about and correctly summarise the data you have collected.
- You comment on your data using the statistics, such as standard deviation, that you have calculated.
- Your comments need to be relevant to the original hypothesis and show an appreciation of how significant they are in terms of the sample used.
- You consider what you have done and make suggestions about how realistic your conclusions are, and suggest ways in which your survey could have been improved, and, if possible, make the improvement.
- You make a statement about how your sample was collected and ways in which this could have been improved.

Is there a connection between foot length and height?

The following task gets a mark of 8 in each strand.

Anna's answer

Aim

I want to find out if there is a connection between people's height and their foot length. I will look at some data from the internet about the foot lengths and heights of 100 children aged between 7 and 16 and see if there is a connection. I will also collect data from pupils at my school and see if there is a connection there.

Hypothesis 1
I predict that taller people have bigger feet. ◄─────

Moderator's TIP
You should always state a hypothesis.

Plan

I will download the data into a file and then analyse this for the 100 children. I will then measure the height and foot length of 30 pupils from my school. If there is a connection then there will be a correlation between foot length and height in both sets of data. To select the pupils from my school I will have to get a list of pupils in alphabetical order and select 30 students at random by

A04 1/7

This plan meets the basic requirements to investigate the hypothesis. The sample size is appropriate (30 is a minimum number), and big enough for a valid conclusion to be reached. The plan allows more advanced statistics to be used (box plots, histograms, product moment correlation coefficient).
(Bullet 1)

assigning a random number to them. It might be that this will not work because I can't be sure the pupils I pick will want to be measured. Some pupils might be embarrassed if they think they are short or tall. If I just asked my friends it might make the information biased. I will analyse the data by working out the mean height and foot length of different ages of boys and girls. I will plot the data on a scatter graph and see if there is a correlation. I will test this by using a product moment correlation coefficient. I will do the same thing for the data taken from pupils at my school. I will also compare the two sets of data using box plots and histograms to see if they compare.

The Internet data is a subset of a huge database of children all over the world. The sample from my school should not be significantly different from the world data.

The data was downloaded from the Internet site 'census in schools'. This is attached as an appendix.

This graph is a scatter graph of the data for all the pupils.

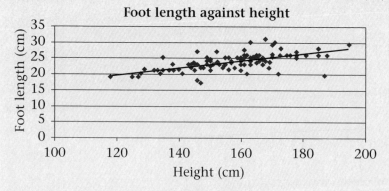

Foot length against height

On the computer I can get a 'product-moment' correlation coefficient (see appendix). The nearer this is to 1 then the better the relationship. For the heights and foot lengths this is 0.606859. This is quite a high number so the taller a person is the bigger their feet are.

The computer can also give me the numbers to draw a line of best fit through the points. This has a slope of 0.11 and an intercept of 6.14. I have drawn a line of best fit through the data that goes through the mean value (156.4, 23.1) which I found from the computer.

I calculated the intercept on my graph to be (100,17).

This graph and the product coefficient prove my hypothesis for the internet data.

A04 3/7

Anna comments on her data and the analysis. This is relevant to the problem. Even though Anna uses a product moment correlation coefficient, which is beyond the GCSE syllabus, she only makes a simple comment and does not make any comparison with it. (Bullet 1)

I have decided to look at the distribution of ages to see if there is any bias in the Internet data. The ages are shown in the bar chart below.

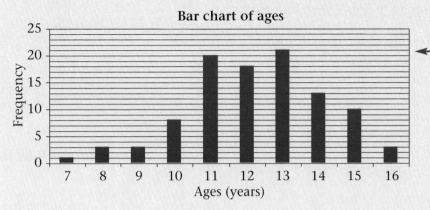

Bar chart of ages

From the bar chart I can see there are more 11, 12, and 13 year olds than any other age group. I want to know if this has affected my analysis and so I have decided to compare the mean heights and foot lengths for each age group.

This table shows the mean foot length and height for each age group.

Age (years)	Number of pupils	Mean height (cm)	Mean foot length (cm)	Mean height/ mean foot length
16	3	172.7	26.0	6.64
15	10	170.1	26.3	6.46
14	13	169.4	23.8	7.12
13	21	160.2	24.3	6.59
12	18	154.7	22.8	6.79
11	20	152.3	23.7	6.43
10	8	144.9	23.6	6.14
9	3	128.0	20.0	6.40
8	3	133.3	21.0	6.35
7	1	127.0	19.0	6.68

The last column shows the mean height ÷ mean foot length. You can see that the values of this for each age group are very similar. They have a mean value of 6.56 and a standard deviation (see appendix) of 0.27. I think it is therefore reasonable to conclude that age does not affect the correlation between height and foot length. Therefore the fact that there are larger numbers of 11, 12, and 13 year olds in the Internet data will not affect my analysis.

However, this has given me the idea to collect data from the pupils in my school from one age group only. I will only collect data from Year 8 pupils; this will probably be easier as I can ask a tutor group to volunteer. I asked the Head of Year and she said that tutor groups are put together fairly randomly so this should not be a biased set of data.

> **A04 1/7**
> Anna changes her plan and recognises the limitations of her original sample. Looking at a particular group of pupils makes the problem a more substantial one.
> (Bullet 3)

Now I am going to look at the data I collected for 12/13 year-olds from my school.

This is my data which I collected from a tutor group one morning. There should have been 31 pupils but four were away so I have only got 27 sets of data.

A	B	C	D
M	12	165	30.0
F	13	174	27.0
M	13	153	26.5
M	13	168	26.0
M	13	161	26.0
M	13	156	26.0
M	12	165	25.0
F	13	158	25.0
M	13	163	24.0
M	13	155	24.0
M	12	151	24.0
F	13	157	23.5
F	12	166	23.0
M	13	160	23.0

A	B	C	D
M	13	157	23.0
F	13	157	23.0
M	12	136	23.0
F	13	166	22.5
M	13	145	22.0
F	12	144	22.0
F	13	142	22.0
M	12	140	21.0
F	13	170	20.5
M	12	144	20.5
F	12	148	18.0
F	12	145	17.0
M	13	177	15.5

A = Gender   B = Age (yrs)
C = Height (cm)   D = Foot length (cm)

> **Moderator's TIP**
> Always define variables in tables.

This is a scatter graph of the above data.

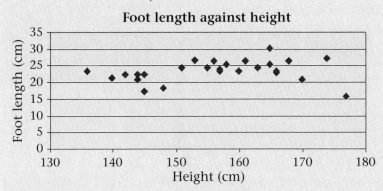

Foot length against height

I used a spreadsheet to draw the scatter graph and then calculate the 'product moment' correlation coefficient. The correlation coefficient was 0.234815. This is not a very strong correlation. There is one piece of data (177, 15.5) which can be considered an outlier. This is because the value for the height ÷ foot length is more than 3 standard deviations away from the mean height ÷ foot length. If I remove this value from the set of data then the correlation coefficient is much stronger: 0.51929. I think that this therefore proves my hypothesis for the data for pupils at my school.

> **A04 2/7**
>
> Anna has spotted a piece of data that may bias the results. The rest of the data is analysed with this piece removed. (Bullet 1)

I want to know if data from the Internet is comparable with the data I collected from my school. I can do this by looking at the box plots of the two sets of data for height and foot length.

The following box plots show the comparisons between the 12/13 year-olds from the Internet and the 12/13 year-olds from my school. I found the information for the box plots using the quartile function on the spreadsheet.

Box plot showing height for Internet data

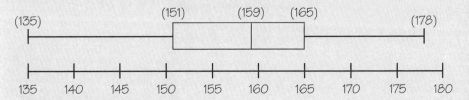

Box plot showing height for pupil data

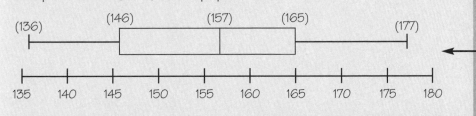

> **A04 2/7**
>
> Anna represents and uses box plots to compare data. (Bullet 3)

These two box plots show that the two sets of data are quite similar. They both have just about the same lowest and highest values. The pupil data is slightly 'skewed' to the left of the median which will probably account for the lower median.

Foot length for internet data

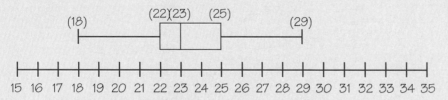

Foot length for pupil data

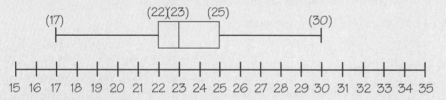

These box plots are identical except for the lowest and highest values.

The box plots

Whilst doing this work I found a web-site that will draw box-plots for you. Unfortunately the box-plots are not to the same scale so they could not be compared easily. However, the box plots did identify outliers for the foot length data. An outlier is a piece of data that is more than 3 standard deviations from the mean.

I decided to compare the averages and correlation between the sets of data again once the outliers were removed.

A04 3/7

Anna compares the two box plots. To get this mark you must be accurate with plotting diagrams and doing calculations. (Bullet 5)

A04 1/7

Anna decides to use new statistical processing techniques as a consequence of her research on the Internet. Her aim is clearly given as looking at the effect of removing outliers when calculating the mean and standard deviation. (Bullet 2)

		Mean height (cm)	Standard deviation height (cm)	Mean foot length (cm)	Standard deviation of foot length (cm)
INTERNET	With outliers	157.6	9.55	23.6	2.52
	Without outliers	158.0	9.43	23.74	1.79
PUPIL	With outliers	156.4	10.81	23.4	2.75
	Without outliers	156.8	10.78	23.7	2.48

There is not much difference between the averages and the standard deviations; although the standard deviation, which is a measure of spread, is lower when the outliers are removed.

> **A04 3/7**
>
> Anna comments on the analysis using Standard Deviation. (Bullet 2)

The correlation coefficients before outliers were removed were 0.52 for the internet data and 0.53 for the pupil data.

The correlation coefficients after outliers were removed were 0.45 for the internet data and 0.40 for the pupil data.

> **A04 2/7**
>
> Anna uses some statistical techniques which are outside the GCSE syllabus. This doesn't in itself guarantee a mark of 7 or more in strand 2 but as Anna has used them appropriately to compare data she gets the mark. The calculations also have to be correct. (Bullet 4)

Surprisingly, the data had a better correlation before the outliers were taken out. This was the opposite to what I thought would happen. However, when I thought about it, outliers have two values and the correlation coefficient is a measure of how related the data is and how close to a line of best fit it is. For example, an outlier such as 17 cm for foot length may also have a small height value so this will fit with the rest of the data on a line of best fit.

The following diagram shows how an outlier makes the line of best fit better.

Line of best fit with outlier included.   **Line of best fit with outlier removed.**

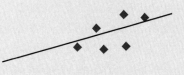

Outlier

> **A04 2/7**
>
> Anna considers the limitations of her data and explains why outliers may affect the mean and standard deviation but may make the correlation better. (Bullet 2)

I have finished my initial analysis and I have some good results. I think my work so far has proved my hypothesis that there is a connection between a person's foot length and height. From my analysis of age distribution I can conclude that age will not affect the correlation between height and foot length. There is no difference between the height of students in my school and the general data. The box plots and the product moment show that the distribution for the foot length is almost the same.

I think it is true to say that a person's foot length has a positive correlation with their height.

<u>Further analysis</u>

I am now going to look at the data for boys and girls separately. I have put all the internet data and the school data for people aged 12 and 13 years together.

I am going to suggest two further hypotheses.

Hypothesis 2: The mean height and mean foot length of girls will be less than that of boys.

Hypothesis 3: The correlation between the height and foot length of boys and girls will not be significantly different.

This is a summary of the results of the boys' and girls' data considered separately.

	Mean height (cm)	SD height (cm)	Skewness height	Mean foot length (cm)	SD foot length (cm)	Skewness foot length
Boys	157.2	15.0	0.27	24.2	2.56	0.29
Girls	156.1	11.4	−1.07	23.0	2.66	−0.09

Hypothesis 2:

The skewness values show that the girls' data is spread out below the mean for height and is just about symmetrical for foot length. The boys' data is spread out above the mean. Skewness is a measure of how the data is spread in comparison to the mean. If a distribution is symmetrical the skewness value is zero. If it is more spread out above the mean than it is below the mean it has a positive skewness value.

AO4 2/7
Throughout the work Anna has linked her diagrams and calculations and has related this to her initial hypothesis. (Bullet 5)

AO4 3/7
Anna pulls all her work together and makes a correct conclusion. This is related back to the original problem and the original hypothesis is justified. (Bullet 3)

AO4 1/7
Anna has decided to combine her internet and pupil data, so she has refined her data. (Bullet 4)

AO4 1/7
Anna looks at a further problem that is related to the initial hypothesis and makes two further hypotheses that involve a more demanding problem that adds depth to the original. (Bullet 2)

Moderator's **TIP**
You should always explain a statistical measure that is outside the GCSE specification.

I will check this by looking at the shapes of the distributions.

The following histograms show the distributions of height and foot length for both boys and girls. These also have the mean marked on, which shows that the data for boys is skewed above the mean and that the girls' data for height is skewed below the mean. The girls' data for foot length is symmetrical about the mean which is backed up by a skewness number that is close to zero.

Histogram showing boys' heights

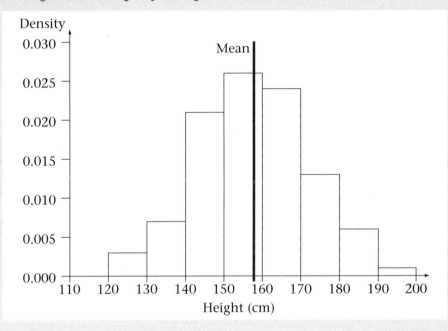

Histogram showing girls' heights

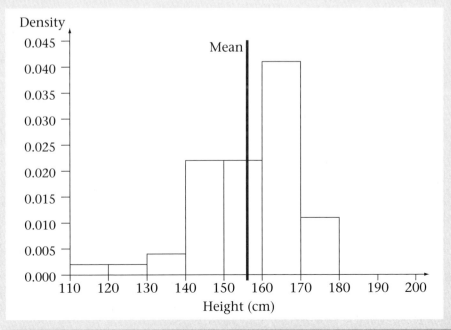

These two histograms show that the girls have a mean height slightly less than that of the boys, but that boys tend to be above the mean and girls tend to be below the mean. However, the shape of the distributions is interesting. The boys' distribution is almost symmetrical and the girls' has a negative skewness. I would need to collect more data to check if this was true for all boys and girls or whether it is just true for this data. I could also compare adult heights. I would expect there to be a difference in the means for adults and that the distributions for both male and female would be symmetrical.

A04 3/7

Anna makes a valid conclusion based on the work she has done and comments on how realistic her conclusion is. (Bullet 4)

Histogram showing boys' foot lengths

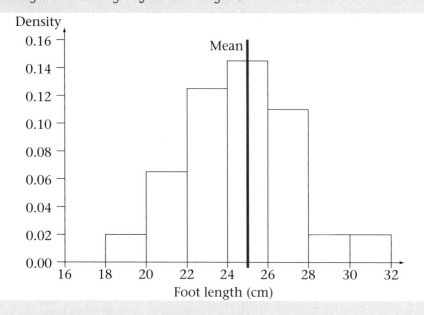

Histogram showing girls' foot lengths

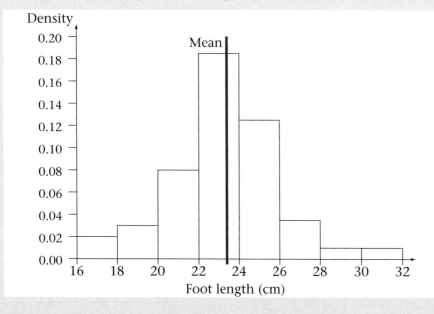

These two histograms show that the size of boys' and girls' feet is very similar, with girls having a mean foot length about 1 cm less than boys. This is only approximately a 2.5% difference, which I do not think is significant. I can therefore conclude that my hypothesis 2 (that mean height and mean foot length for girls will be less than that of boys) is incorrect. There is no significant difference.

However, this data was only from 130 people. I could look at a much wider sample. The 'censusinschool' website, for instance, has thousands of sets of data. Using this would basically give the mean and distributions for the heights and foot lengths of the population of children throughout the world. (A population is everyone; a sample is a representative selection from this).

Hypothesis 3:

The correlation coefficient between height and foot length for girls is 0.51. The correlation coefficient between height and foot length for boys is 0.65.

Since the correlation between height and foot length is positive, the range of possible values is 0–1. This means the correlation coefficients differ by 14%. I think this is a significant difference, so I can conclude that the correlation between the boys' height and foot length is stronger than that of the girls.

Hypothesis testing – two sample test of means

Whilst I was looking for information on the internet I came across a statistical analysis package. This gave me lots of options, one of which was a 'two sample test of means'.

I looked into this in more detail. What this does is test if two distributions could have come from the same population. This means that I can ask the question: Are the school data and the internet data consistent with each other? This analysis will be more accurate than the analysis I did before.

To do this I need to set up a null hypothesis and an alternative hypothesis. The null hypothesis is that the means of the populations from which the two distributions are taken are the same. The alternative hypothesis is that the means are not the same.

The test is done at the 5% level. This means that the data will appear to be from different populations 5 in 100 times even if they are from the same population.

A04 3/7

Anna considers the nature of her data and how it could be improved.
(Bullet 5)

A04 1/8

Anna has covered all the bullet points for A04 1/7 and 1/8. By looking at a far more demanding problem that is well explained and shows understanding of hypothesis testing Anna gets a mark of 8 in strand 1.

A04 2/8

Anna has covered all the bullet points for A04 2/7 and 2/8. By using mathematics beyond the GCSE syllabus correctly and explaining the different aspects of the hypothesis test are will give a mark of 8 in strand 2.

There are two statistics that the data returns. The first is the p-value which is the probability that the null hypothesis is true. It also gives a t-value which is a test based on the number of pieces of data, the means and the standard deviations. If the t-value or p-value is less than 0.05 then the test fails and the alternative hypothesis is accepted.

For a comparison of the heights of the Internet data and the pupil data the values are

p-value	0.6269
t-value	0.4775

This means we can accept the null hypothesis that the two sets of data for height are from the same population. I would expect very similar results if I compare the foot length data. In fact, comparing the foot lengths gives a p-value of 0.8104 and a t-value of 0.2409. Once again we can conclude that the two sets of data are from the same population.

Conclusion

As would have been expected there was no statistical difference between the pupil data, which was taken from a small tutor group at my school, and the Internet data which has been supplied by children all over the world. From this I can conclude that 12/13 year-old children all over the world have the same height and foot length correlation. It is not clear if the Internet data is representative of the world's 12/13 year olds, as poorer children may not have access to the internet. I might expect poorer children to be less well nourished and so be smaller and have smaller feet. This would not affect the correlation – it would just increase the range of distribution. This means that my data is probably not biased, but is also not entirely representative.

A04 3/8

Anna has covered all the bullets for A04 3/7 and 3/8. By making a correct analysis and relating this to the original problem Anna gets a mark of 8 in strand 3. The calculations must be correct and the statistical data must be correctly interpreted.

Moderator's TIP

Write a conclusion linking your results to the original hypothesis and consider the limitations of your original data.

Checklist for the A04 task
Higher tier

Planning

☐ Have you chosen a project that will allow you to use advanced statistical techniques, and to show creative thinking?

☐ Have you stated your hypothesis?

☐ Have you decided what data you will need, how you will collect it, what size your sample should be, and how you will avoid bias?

☐ Do you need to do a pre-test or design a questionnaire?

☐ Have you written a clear and detailed plan, and given reasons for your choice of plan?

Processing

☐ Have you taken variability and bias in your data into account?

☐ Have you considered the limitations on your data, and considered how your method of sampling will affect the reliability of the data?

☐ Have you represented and analysed the data using histograms, standard deviation, product moment correlation coefficient, skewness and other techniques?

☐ Are all your calculations and diagrams correct?

☐ Have you checked that there are no irrelevant calculations and diagrams in your report?

Interpreting

☐ Have you commented on and summarised your results?

☐ Have you linked all the diagrams and calculations together and related them back to the original problem?

☐ Have you considered your strategy and suggested ways in which it could be improved?

☐ Have you considered how realistic your conclusions are?

☐ Have you written about the limitations of the strategy you have chosen?

Handling data using spreadsheets

If you want to make life easy for yourself then you can use a spreadsheet to process and analyse your data. Spreadsheets will do just about any statistical analysis.

You should work through the following sections and make sure you can use a spreadsheet. These are all based on the Microsoft EXCEL spreadsheet, which is the most common one in use.

Basic techniques

Enter the raw data from the first list below into cells A1 to A10 and B1 to B10. This is some data that links height (column A) with foot length (column B).

Sorting

Highlight *all* the data in cells A1 to B10. In 'DATA' from the menu bar click on 'Sort'. A menu pops up that will ask you which column to sort by and whether you want it to be in ascending or descending order. Choose 'column A' and 'descending'. Click 'OK' and the data will sort itself into the second list below.

	A	B
1	165	26
2	160	24.5
3	147	22
4	157	23
5	145	21
6	156	21.5
7	140	22
8	157	23.5
9	167	23
10	159	24

	A	B
1	167	23
2	165	26
3	160	24.5
4	159	24
5	157	23
6	157	23.5
7	156	21.5
8	147	22
9	145	2321
10	140	22

Note that the values in column A are sorted into their descending order and the values in column B stay alongside the corresponding value in column A. It is important to highlight all the data before sorting; otherwise linked data may get shuffled about and split.

Sorting can be useful for putting data in order when you want to work out medians and quartiles.

Functions

There are lots of functions you can use on a spreadsheet to get statistical information. Functions all work in much the same way.

This is explained in detail with the functions QUARTILE and PEARSON. Other functions are listed in the table on page 64 with their main features.

Using the data entered (raw or sorted) above:

- Click into cell A11.
- Type '='

- From 'Insert' on the menu bar choose 'Function'. A dialogue box comes up.
- Choose 'Statistical' from the left-hand list.
- Choose QUARTILE from the right-hand list.
- Click OK and another dialogue box comes up.
- Enter A1:A10 in the first blank window.
- Enter 1 in the second window.
- Press OK and in the cell A11 you should see 149.25, which is the *lower quartile* of the data in cells A1 to A10.
- Entering 2 in the second window returns the *median*.
- Entering 3 returns the *upper quartile*.
- Entering 0 returns the *minimum value*.
- Entering 4 returns the *maximum value*.

You can find the range of the data using = MAX(A1:A10)–MIN(A1:A10).

PEARSON

This is the function that gives the rank correlation coefficient described. Enter the following data into cells A1 to B10:

	A	B
1	7	6
2	5	4
3	3	2
4	1	3
5	8	7
6	4	1
7	2	5
8	9	10
9	10	9
10	6	8

- Click into cell A11.
- Type '='
- From 'Insert' on the menu bar choose 'Function'. A dialogue box comes up.
- Choose 'Statistical' from the left-hand list.
- Choose PEARSON from the right-hand list.
- Click OK and another dialogue box comes up.
- Enter A1:A10 in the first window (Array 1).
- Enter B1:B10 in the second window (Array 2).
- Press OK and in the cell A11 you should see 0.806060606, which is the (Pearson) rank correlation coefficient.

Other functions

The principal functions that you will find useful in analysing statistical data are listed on page 64. You are advised to work through each one and make sure you can use the spreadsheet to work them out. The processes are described for Microsoft EXCEL spreadsheets which is the most common in use. Newer versions may do some of the operations described above, such as entering data labels, automatically.

Representing data

You can also use spreadsheets to represent your data.

To draw a bar chart

Start a new spreadsheet. Enter the following raw data into cells A1 to B5.

	A	B
1	Red	2
2	Blue	4
3	Green	5
4	Black	3
5	Silver	7

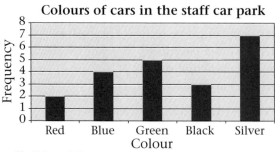

- Highlight the values in cells B1 to B5.
- From 'Insert' on the menu bar choose 'Chart'. The first chart, which is already highlighted, is 'Column'. (Ignore the one that says 'Bar').
- There are several choices on the style of column chart. Leave it on the one that is already highlighted for now. Click NEXT and a dialogue box comes up. This shows you a picture of the bar chart but there are no labels.
- Click on the tab at the top that says SERIES. Another dialogue box comes up. In the blank window labelled NAME: type 'Colours of cars'.
- In the blank window labelled CATEGORY (X) AXIS LABELS: type '=Sheet1!$A$1:$A$5'. (This is the same as the VALUES: window but with B replaced with A).
- Click NEXT. Another dialogue box comes up.
- Click on the tab at the top that says TITLES.
- Click into the CHART TITLE: window and type 'Colours of cars in the staff car park'.
- Click in to the CATEGORY (X) AXIS: window and type 'Colours'.
- Click into the Value (Y) AXIS: window and type 'Frequency'.
- Click NEXT. Ignore the next dialogue box.
- Click on FINISH and the chart shown above should appear on the spreadsheet. By grabbing it with mouse you can position it anywhere you like or, when it is highlighted, copy it into another document.

To draw a pie chart

Start a new spreadsheet. Enter the following raw data into cells A1 to B5.

	A	B
1	Dog	6
2	Cat	9
3	Rabbit	2
4	Fish	8
5	Horse	5

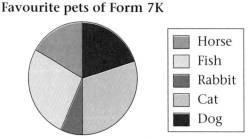

- Highlight the values in cells B1 to B5.
- From Insert on the menu bar choose 'Chart'. Choose PIE. There are several choices on the style of pie chart. Leave it on the one that is already highlighted for now.
- Click NEXT and a dialogue box comes up. This shows you a picture of the pie chart but there are no labels.

- Click on the tab at the top that says SERIES. Another dialogue box comes up.
- In the blank window labelled NAME: type 'Pets'.
- In the blank window labelled CATEGORY LABELS: type '=Sheet1!$A$1:$A$5'. (This is the same as the VALUES: window but with B replaced with A).
- Click NEXT. Another dialogue box comes up.
- Click on the tab at the top that says TITLES.
- Click into the CHART TITLE: window and type 'Favourite pets of Form 7K'.
- Click NEXT. Ignore the next dialogue box.
- Click on FINISH and the chart shown above should appear on the spreadsheet. By grabbing it with mouse you can position it anywhere you like, or if it is highlighted copy it into another document.

To draw a scatter graph

Start a new spreadsheet. Enter the raw data below into cells A1 to B5.
- Highlight the values in cells A1 to B5.
- From Insert on the menu bar choose 'Chart'.
- Choose XY(SCATTER). There are several choices on the style of scatter graph. Leave it on the one that is already highlighted for now.
- Click NEXT and a dialogue box comes up.

	A	B
1	12	3.7
2	17	4.5
3	14	3.9
4	28	6.2
5	21	5.9

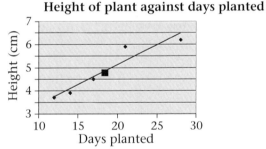

Height of plant against days planted

- Click on the tab at the top that says SERIES. Another dialogue box comes up.
- In the blank window labelled NAME: type 'Height'.
- Click on NEXT. Another dialogue box comes up.
- In the window labelled CHART TITLE: type 'Height of plant against days planted'.
- In the blank window labelled VALUE (X) AXIS: type 'Days planted'.
- In the blank window labelled VALUE (Y): type 'Height (cm)'.
- Click on FINISH and the scatter graph shown above should appear on the spreadsheet. By grabbing it with mouse you can position it anywhere you like, or if it is highlighted copy it into a word processing document.

You can use Excel to find the features of the line of best fit of your scatter graph. You can use =INTERCEPT(B1:B5,A1:A5) to find the intercept of the line of best fit with the *y*-axis. You can use =SLOPE(B1:B5,A1:A5) to get the gradient of the line of best fit. For the above data this would give a line of best fit with equation:

$y = 0.17x + 1.68$

This line has been drawn through the data. Lines of best fit should also go through the average *x*-value and the average *y*-value. Using =AVERAGE(A1:A5) and =AVERAGE(B1:B5), this point is (18.4, 4.8). This point has also been plotted on the graph (as a square).

Other statistical diagrams such as frequency polygons, box plots, cumulative frequency diagrams and histograms have to be drawn by hand, although you can get the necessary data for plotting from the spreadsheet.

Function	First blank window	Second blank window	What it gives you	Example. (Your function will look like this or you can type this in directly.)	Result for data on p60 (rounded)
MIN	Range of values	Not applicable	The smallest value of the data	=MIN(A1:A10)	140
MAX	Range of values	Not applicable	The largest value of the data	=MAX(A1:A10)	167
COUNT	Range of values	Not applicable	The number of pieces of data in the set	=COUNT(A1:A10)	10
MODE	Range of values	Not applicable	The modal value of the data. #N/A means no mode	=MODE(A1:A10)	157
MEDIAN	Range of values	Not applicable	The median value of the data	=MEDIAN(A1:A10)	157
QUARTILE	Range of values	0	The smallest value of the data	=QUARTILE(A1:A10,0)	140
QUARTILE	Range of values	1	The lower quartile of the data	=QUARTILE(A1:A10,1)	149.25
QUARTILE	Range of values	2	The median value of the data	=QUARTILE(A1:A10,2)	157
QUARTILE	Range of values	3	The upper quartile of the data	=QUARTILE(A1:A10,3)	159.75
QUARTILE	Range of values	4	The largest value of the data	=QUARTILE(A1:A10,4)	167
SUM	Range of values	Not applicable	The total of all the values	=SUM(A1:A10)	1553
AVERAGE	Range of values	Not applicable	The mean value of the data	=AVERAGE(A1:A10)	155.3
STDEV	Range of values	Not applicable	The standard deviation of the data	=STDEV(A1:A10)	8.705
SKEW	Range of values	Not applicable	A measure of the skewness of the data	=SKEW(A1:A10)	−0.540
CORREL	Range of data of x values	Range of data of y values	The product moment correlation coefficient	=CORREL(A1:A10,B1:B10)	0.705
SLOPE	Range of data of y values	Range of data of x values	The slope of the line of best fit through the data	=SLOPE(B1:B10,A1:A10)	0.123
INTERCEPT	Range of data of y values	Range of data of x values	The intercept on the y-axis of the line of best fit through the data	=INTERCEPT(B1:B10,A1:A10)	3.959

NOTE: SUM is found in the Maths & Trig menu.